T

Perfectly Imperfect

Marion Reeves

For Avery

Perfectly Imperfect

Marion Reeves

Ambassador International
GREENVILLE, SOUTH CAROLINA & BELFAST, NORTHERN IRELAND

www.ambassador-international.com

Perfectly Imperfect

© 2017 by Marion Reeves
All rights reserved

ISBN: 978-1-62020-583-9
eISBN: 978-1-62020-658-4

Cover Design and Page Layout by Hannah Nichols
eBook Conversion by Anna Riebe Raats
Author Photo by Peden Wright

AMBASSADOR INTERNATIONAL
Emerald House
411 University Ridge, Suite B14
Greenville, SC 29601, USA
www.ambassador-international.com

AMBASSADOR BOOKS
The Mount
2 Woodstock Link
Belfast, BT6 8DD, Northern Ireland, UK
www.ambassadormedia.co.uk
The colophon is a trademark of Ambassador

This book is dedicated to Rob and Barbara Reeves, the best parents in the entire world. Thank you for believing in me, supporting me, loving me, and being my biggest cheerleaders. I love y'all so much.

Acknowledgments

When looking back at every stage in my life that has led me to where I am now, I have realized that I would not be where I am today without the support of a number of people. A simple thank you can't encompass how grateful I am for the support and love I have received from so many along the way. I never imagined I would be here writing this book and telling my story the way I am now. But this isn't just my story. This story has a lot of other supporting characters in it who deserve recognition.

To my parents—I wouldn't be where I am today without y'all. Thank you for providing me with the help and resources I needed to get better and for never giving up on me.

To my brothers—Austin and Crawford, thanks for always trying to make me laugh, even at the times where I didn't want to.

To my sister-in-law—Jenn, thank you for being the big sister I have always wanted. You are the best!

To all of my friends who stuck with me through it all—Thank y'all for never turning your back on me, even when I was absolutely no fun to be around.

To Ella Walker Henderson—Thank you for not only being a great therapist, but for also being someone that I look up to in so many ways. Thank you for showing me what it looks like to truly have a relationship with the Lord. And thank you for your input and advice throughout the editing process.

To Rob Henderson—Thank you for being an encourager, for listening to me, and for praying for me.

To Scott Dobson—Thank you for not only being my doctor, but a constant support throughout all stages of the recovery process.

To Darren DePaul—Thank you for constantly pouring into me spiritually and reminding me that following my eating disorder wasn't worth it but following Jesus is. Thank you for helping me to see that my joy can ultimately be found only in the Lord.

To MK Billings, Emily Geyer, and Brooke Teague—Thanks for always listening to me, pointing me back to Jesus, and for giving the best advice.

To Kathryn Short, Christina Cown, and Myra Hendley—Thank y'all for being patient with me (even when I was extremely stubborn and unwilling to change) and for helping me learn how to function apart from my eating disorder.

To Coach Ed Boehmke and Coach Travis Alexander—Thank you for showing me that I am capable of more than I think and stronger than I think, both in running and in life.

To Kevin Licht—Thank you for helping me fall back in love with running again after it became something it wasn't supposed to be.

To Keith Williams—thank you for showing me that exercise could be fun again and done in a healthy way to make my body stronger, not to tear it down.

And most importantly to God—there is no way I would be where I am today without You.

Contents

FOREWORD

I AM BLESSED TO KNOW Marion in multiple capacities, first as her therapist and later as director during her internship at Living Bread, a non-profit that serves eating disorders in the upstate of South Carolina. It was her struggle with an eating disorder that brought us together but her desire to serve others that gave us a renewed unity of purpose.

Marion has a passion for life. She inspires strength in others. She emanates a gentle quiet that reassures those around her. She has a natural sense of bravery. She desires to change the lives of others, to offer hope and courage to those who have none. She was in their place once and believes others have a chance at a new life, just like her, especially when it comes to eating disorders.

Eating disorders are brushed aside by many in our society. They believe that an eating disorder will go away if someone "just eats normally." However, eating disorders are a complex illness that require in-depth treatment. They impact all areas of life and functioning, especially family life. Marion presents a real story to show you the pervasive impact of an eating disorder in her own life. By doing this, she helps others to see that eating disorders are not something a teenager (or adult) will grow out of or something that's "just a phase." The earlier someone seeks help, the better the treatment outcome. Eating disorders require professional help and, more than that, require a person to face some of their biggest fears. Recovery takes courage and the support of loved ones.

Eating disorders are a growing and serious problem in our society and are highly connected to dieting behaviors and body image. According to the National Eating Disorder Association (www.nationaleatingdisorders.org):

- The prevalence of eating disorders is similar among Non-Hispanic Whites, Hispanics, African-Americans, and Asians in the United States, with the exception that anorexia nervosa is more common among Non-Hispanic Whites.

- In the United States, 20 million women and 10 million men suffer from a clinically significant eating disorder at some time in their life.

- A review of nearly fifty years of research confirms that anorexia nervosa has the highest mortality rate of any psychiatric disorder.

- For females between fifteen to twenty-four years old who suffer from anorexia nervosa, the mortality rate associated with the illness is twelve times higher than the death rate of all other causes of death.

- 42% of 1st-3rd grade girls want to be thinner.

- 81% of 10 year olds are afraid of being fat.

- 46% of 9-11 year-olds are "sometimes" or "very often" on diets, and 82% of their families are "sometimes" or "very often" on diets.

- Over one-half of teenage girls and nearly one-third of teenage boys use unhealthy weight control behaviors such as skipping meals, fasting, smoking cigarettes, vomiting, and taking laxatives.

Eating disorders and what they leave in their psychological wake are more common and impactful than we realize. Be a part of making a difference by spreading awareness and journeys of recovery like Marion's.

This is a story of bravery and courage: how one girl stopped letting an eating disorder take over her life and found freedom. This is a story about a girl who discovered that God's love was worth sacrificing everything for, even control. She couldn't do it alone. I'm one of countless others who bear witness to her journey.

Read on. Spread the courage.

— Ella Walker Henderson, M.A., LPC

Founder, Counselor

Living Bread

Chapter One

THE BEGINNING

IF YOU LOOK AT THE life I lived from the time I was born up until I was thirteen years old, you would have seen a carefree little girl who believed that she had her whole life ahead of her. You would have seen a girl who had a smile that could light up a room. A girl who loved spending time with her friends and family. A girl who had a brain that wasn't tainted by the societal expectations of how her body should look or what she should eat. I was a normal girl, who did normal things such as . . .

- Going shopping with my mom and then going out to lunch at our favorite Japanese restaurant
- Asking my dad to take me to TCBY after school every Wednesday for Waffle Cone Wednesday
- Getting doughnuts on the way to school
- Sitting on the couch with a bag of Goldfish crackers, eating until I was satisfied
- Getting excited about going to my favorite restaurant for dinner

- Not caring about the size of my jeans, just caring about how they fit me
- Not having any idea what the number on the scale said
- Not labeling any foods as "good" or "bad"
- Just being normal

I didn't have a care in the world about the food I was putting in my body. If I was hungry, I would eat. If I wasn't hungry, then I wouldn't. What a simple concept. I trusted my body to let me know when it was time to eat. I didn't know what a calorie was for the longest time. And even when I learned what it was, I didn't pay attention to the number that was on the package or box or wrapper of my favorite foods.

I was an active child, playing every sport you could imagine. I danced, I played soccer, I played basketball, I ran, I played golf . . . you name it, I did it. But I never felt like it was a requirement for me to do any of those things. I played all those sports and did all my activities simply because they were fun. It wasn't to maintain a certain body weight. It wasn't to burn off the food I had eaten. I was never overweight, or even "chubby," for that matter. I was just a kid.

But then something changed.

Maybe it started in a dressing room one day. Or maybe it started the first time I stepped on a scale and saw that my weight was no longer in the double digits. Maybe it started when I began comparing myself to friends who were thinner than I was. Dressing rooms became a struggle for me. I had in my head the size that I was. If I tried on that specific size and it didn't fit, I was a failure. I can remember many times where I ended up in tears while shopping with my mom because I had to get a bigger size. According to my brain, the pants weren't the problem; my body was. I remember getting weighed in our PE class one year, and that was the day when I saw my weight shift to the 100s. I thought that meant I was getting fat. Little did I know, it just meant that I was growing like I should have been. I remember being at the pool with friends, or in dance class, and comparing myself to the way the other girls looked. I was too big. There was a problem with my body. I started becoming insecure with the way I looked.

I started running cross country when I was in 7th grade. It was a way for me to be a part of a team, and I enjoyed running. My 7th grade season was fun. I wasn't the best on the team, but I wasn't the worst either. I was consistently improving and able to run faster and longer each day. I was fueling my body for the amount of exercise I was doing, and everything was great. However, many people think that if you are thinner, you will run faster. And while, to an extent, that can be true at first, if you continue to lose weight unhealthily, you will get burnt out. But I was willing to do whatever it took to get faster. So the summer before I entered the 8th grade, I set out on a mission to have the perfect "runner's body." Looking back, I wish I had known that the perfect "runner's body" doesn't exist. You don't have to look a certain way to be a runner.

The trigger of running, combined with my perfectionistic personality, a negative body-image, and the fact that I was entering the phase in my life where I was supposed to be growing and developing into a woman, ended up creating the perfect storm for the development of an eating disorder. I didn't set out to develop an eating disorder. Eating disorders aren't a choice. I didn't choose the months and years of misery that would ensue. It was just a simple, innocent plan to lose a little weight and tone up before the cross country season started again in the fall. I wish I could say I vaguely remember the day that took me off course, but I don't vaguely remember it. I remember it *vividly*.

I had gone to the lake with my best friend for Memorial Day weekend. It was finally getting warm enough to swim and enjoy the lake. I remember going to Zaxby's on the way to the lake and getting what I would normally get—a Big Zak Snack with a sweet tea. I didn't think anything of it. It was just food, a normal meal for me. We got to the lake about an hour later and spent a good bit of the afternoon swimming in the pool at the lake house before going out in the boat. After swimming for a little while, it was time for some snacks. We laid our towels out on the chairs by the pool, sat down, and started snacking. I don't remember all of the snacks that were on hand, but I do remember eating two specific things: Doritos and marshmallows. Great combination, huh? I wasn't overeating or binging. I was simply doing what a normal teenager would do, chowing down on delicious snacks while having a great time with my best friend.

Once we got full, we decided just to lie there in the chairs by the pool for a bit. I wish I had known that it was just bloating at the time, but I saw my stomach sticking out over my bathing suit bottoms. I was horrified. I didn't say anything, and I didn't act differently that day at the lake, but that was the day I knew that something needed to change. I didn't want to be "fat" anymore.

It began with just cutting out the foods that I started to perceive as unhealthy based on what I had seen in TV commercials, read in magazines, and heard about in casual conversation. It began with not snacking as much, not drinking sweet tea anymore, and drastically increasing the amount of running I was doing. I was playing AAU basketball at the time, and our season was about to finish up. In addition to basketball practices, I would go for a run as well.

Things were great at first. I was on a "health kick," but I still would treat myself to some of my favorite foods once in a while. Then things started to get dangerous. I started counting calories. I learned about nutrition labels and knew them like the back of my hand. I created an account on a calorie-counting website. I couldn't go to bed at night without logging every single thing I ate and knowing the amount of calories that were in my body, as well as the number of calories I burned off through running.

For the sake of keeping this book as trigger-free as possible for those who might be struggling with eating disorders as well, I am not going to write about specific calorie amounts or say how much weight I was losing. In the grand scheme of things, those numbers aren't important. But I will say that the amount I was eating was nowhere near sufficient to support the amount of activity I participated in and the amount of work my body was exerting. My body was exerting energy to run, but what I didn't realize at the time was that our bodies also exert energy simply to keep us alive. Our bodies use energy so that we can walk, talk, write, laugh, sing, think . . . our bodies support all of our many functions.

I limited myself to a certain number of calories each day. As time went on, that number crept lower and lower. It almost became a competition with myself to see how much less I could get away with than the day before. I got a sense of pleasure, as sick and twisted as it sounds, from seeing the number drop lower.

Running was no longer something fun. It became something I required myself to do each day. If I didn't run, I didn't deserve my food. I started to dread running. I had no energy but ran anyway. I got out of bed every morning to attend cross country conditioning at 7:00 and run the maximum amount that I could. I would come back home and have a small breakfast, shower, and then sleep until it was time for lunch.

My summer was spent watching the clock and waiting for my next meal. My body was craving food, and it was all I could think about. I became obsessed with food. I watched Food Network all the time, I read cookbooks from cover to cover, and I spent hours and hours researching restrictive diets and calorie counting. We didn't have a scale at my house, but I still had a way of checking my weight every once in a while. There was a scale in my grandmother's bathroom at my grandparents' house. Because my grandmother's health was deteriorating at the time, we visited her a good bit. So each time we were there, I would have to go to the bathroom to see what the number said. I wanted to see how quickly my restricting and excessive exercise were leading to weight loss.

Some of the houses where I would babysit had a scale. There was another chance to see the number. My life became nothing but numbers . . . the number of miles I ran, the number of calories I ate, the number on the scale. It was not a fun way to live.

With my strict regimen of running and eating very little, weight began to fall off of me. At first, it seemed like a good thing. I had lost weight, but not enough for it to look "bad" or unhealthy. I had simply trimmed down and toned up. Had I stopped there and returned to normal eating, maybe things would have ended up differently. But I couldn't stop. I had an addiction. I was addicted to restricting. Addicted to calorie counting. Addicted to exercising. And like any other addiction, it is nearly impossible to stop cold-turkey.

Toward the end of the summer and as 8th grade started, my diet spiraled out of control. I no longer allowed myself treats of any kind. I stuck to the same safe foods every single day. Any variation from that sent me into fits of anxiety. Everything had to be perfect. I had to be in control.

The cross country season started off great, which did nothing but fuel my obsession. I saw that my times had dropped, and I was possibly going to get the chance to be in the top seven, so I had to continue doing what had gotten me to that point. The restriction continued like it had, but the mileage increased as the season went on. To this day, I have no idea how I made it through some of our workouts and long runs on the food that I had consumed. I have no idea why I didn't pass out or have a heart attack. I give all the glory to God for that. He had a plan for me, and 8th grade was way too soon to take me away from this earth.

As the cross country season went on and became more intense, so did my anxiety. There were days when I would be sobbing in the car before practice. There were races when I would cry uncontrollably. I don't exactly know what was causing the anxiety in those situations, but I couldn't handle what was going on anymore.

My body started to deteriorate, and my times stagnated and slowed. I lost my spot in the top seven and didn't get to run at the state championship that year, which had been one of my goals. I remember my coach telling me one day after practice, "Marion, if you get any skinnier you could hide behind a spaghetti noodle!" Clearly, there was a problem. But I didn't want to do anything about it.

As I lost weight, I began to lose friends. I wasn't the same person they had gotten to know when they became friends with me. I didn't laugh at their jokes anymore. I didn't ever want to hang out with them. I was scared that they would realize the problem I had. I was scared of the opportunities to eat that might come up if I was with them, but I couldn't tell them that. I was secretive. And after turning down invitation after invitation to hang out, my friends stopped inviting me.

I began to lose the light in my eyes. I lost strength. I was losing everything, yet I couldn't stop. I had already gotten down to a number that I had deemed would be where I would stop losing weight, but I had already spiraled out of control and got a sick sense of satisfaction and accomplishment from each pound that fell off my body. I could no longer handle what was going on. But like I said, I couldn't stop.

Were there times when I wanted to stop? Yes. But I physically couldn't. I didn't realize it yet, but I had a severe, dangerous eating disorder. It held me tight in its grip and had no intention of letting go. Every time I attempted to do something to go against what my eating disorder told me, it seemed to readjust its grip and take hold of me even tighter. I was starting to unravel from the inside out.

Chapter Two

SHOOTING HOOPS

IT WAS EARLY NOVEMBER, AND cross country season had just ended. With the end of cross country season came the beginning of middle school basketball season. Basketball was always something that I looked forward to. I started playing basketball at a very young age, loved watching my two older brothers play basketball, and frequently attended Clemson basketball games with my dad. The announcement that basketball tryouts were coming up came over the intercom at my middle school one morning, and I immediately knew that I needed to practice. I hadn't touched a basketball in four months.

Previously, that wouldn't have really mattered because I knew that I would be able to pick up a ball and remember what to do. My skills might have deteriorated a little, but it wasn't anything that I couldn't pick back up quickly. But for some reason, this time I knew it was going to be different. My dad and I went to shoot basketball at our church gym one night so that I could practice before tryouts started. I wasn't worried about making the team since I had made the starting five a good bit during my 7th grade year. I had played on an AAU team, practicing multiple times a week during the spring and had gained a lot of skills and experience. Yet, when I picked up that basketball the night we went to shoot around, something felt odd. The basketball, which weighed only a little over a pound, felt like a bowling ball.

I started dribbling, and everything seemed fine at first. Then I went to shoot a three-pointer. I had always been a shooter. Sure, I could handle the ball decently and could play point guard if needed, but my specialty was sitting on the wing, waiting for the pass, and firing the shot. *Swish.* I loved shooting three-pointers especially. Ever since I was very young and playing basketball in the driveway with my older brothers, I would always try to shoot from as far back as they were. And eventually, I could get it there.

So I stood there behind the three-point line. Ball in my hands, I aimed for the basket, and released the ball. Air ball. It didn't even come close to hitting the rim. Hmm. Maybe I was just stiff from not shooting in a while, and that was the first shot I took to begin with. I warmed up some more by shooting shots from shorter distances. Things were decent, but I felt like I was using a lot more force to get it up there than I had in the past. Once I got my confidence back from shooting the closer shots, I decided to try the three-pointer again. Here we go. I shot. Air ball again. Not only was it a blatant air ball, but my dad could also tell that my form, the way I was shooting, was different from what it had been in the past. Instead of having a smooth jump shot, releasing the ball in the air and then coming back down, my legs were flailing, as if I were trying to use every fiber of my being to get the ball there. I didn't even know what to say. I couldn't explain what was going on.

That moment was when my dad finally admitted to himself that there was a problem. My strength was gone. What used to be simple for me had become extremely challenging. I don't think I hit the rim on one three-pointer that I shot that night. So not only was it extremely challenging, but on that night, it was impossible. I had to get my strength back up, but deep down I knew that the only way that would happen would be for me to gain weight back. And I sure as heck did not want to do that. I thought maybe doing pushups would help. Sure, pushups might make you stronger. But the thing is, when basketball tryouts are in seven days, doing a few pushups a day isn't going to help much.

The day of basketball tryouts came. I was nervous. Originally I had been confident, knowing that I had been on the team the previous year. The coach knew me and knew what I was capable of. She knew I could shoot, she knew I could dribble, and she knew I could knock down some free-throws. I once made twenty-four out of twenty-five free-throws in practice the year before and won free Chick-fil-A because of it. But it was obvious that I wasn't the same player I had been the year before.

We started out with some running and ball handling drills. Sure, I still had my speed and endurance since I had just come off of cross country season, and my ball handling hadn't suffered too much. But my coach already knew something was off. I remember standing in line waiting for a drill when she came up to me and asked why I had lost so much weight. I gave her the typical answer that I gave to everyone who asked me that question. It seemed like more and more people were asking me that or asking my parents that. "Oh, it's just from running cross country!" I would reply. Maybe it wasn't totally a lie because, yes, running was a catalyst in my extreme weight loss, but that wasn't the complete truth. She didn't seem to buy what I was saying, but she didn't ask any more questions, thankfully. I was off the hook for the time being.

We started doing some more basketball tryout activities like defensive slides, three-man weave, and scrimmaging. It wasn't a complete travesty because I still ended up making the team at the end of the week. But if I wanted to have my starting position back, let alone play in general and not sit on the bench the whole season, I was going to have to work my butt off.

The problem with the idea of working really hard to get back to my previous basketball ability lay in the fact that I had nothing to work with. I had no energy. Basketball practice became this thing I had to do each day that was like a dark raincloud looming over my head. It was a weird feeling. All I wanted to do was go home after school, lie on the couch, and maybe eat a snack if I felt like I deserved it that day. But at the same time, basketball practice was necessary because that was a way to burn calories.

Things got to where I didn't even get to participate that much in basketball practice. Since I wasn't in the starting five, or even the second group of five, I rarely had a chance to scrimmage at practice. I sat on the sidelines with some of the other girls who didn't get to play that much and watched. The only things I ended up doing at practice were the shooting drills at the beginning, the five laps we would run around the gym, and occasionally I'd get to be on one of the teams scrimmaging for a few minutes.

The idea of not doing much at practice freaked me out. Going from running around ten miles a day at cross country practice to "barely doing anything" sent me into a panic. I began to run on my own after basketball practice. The logic I had in my head was this: since I wasn't burning nearly as many calories playing basketball as I was during cross country, I didn't need to eat as much. This logic was fallible for two reasons; first, I already wasn't eating nearly enough, and second, I was still active and running some, just not in the same way that I had before. That didn't mean that I wasn't burning calories still. But to someone with extremely disordered thoughts regarding food and exercise, none of that registered.

Parts of my lunch would get "left at home." Breakfast would get a little bit smaller. Maybe I would have a smaller portion at dinner. More "fear foods" were cut out of my diet. Things had already been out of control before, but at this point, things were really bad.

I didn't think this at the time, but looking back at pictures, I looked extremely sick. I don't know how anyone could have looked at me and not seen that something was severely wrong, especially if it was someone who had seen me before the weight loss took place. I remember a few of my teachers walking by the table I sat at during lunch and inconspicuously trying to peer over my shoulder to make sure I was eating.

This is a good time to point out that at this time in my life, I never completely stopped eating. A common misconception is that someone with an eating disorder doesn't eat at all. That's not true. If someone stopped eating completely, it would be really obvious that there was a problem, and they would die. People with eating disorders actually do eat, and I was no exception to that. I ate lunch every day at school, but that didn't mean that I was getting enough nutrition. It's possible to eat and still lose weight, especially if you aren't eating enough calories and are exercising.

So with that said, none of my teachers could "bust me" at lunch for not eating. Some of my friends would come up behind me in the hallway and grab my waist and say, "you're so little!" which only fueled my eating disorder even more. My eating disorder would let me have a moment to feel accomplished because people told me I was small, but then it was back to the grind of getting even smaller.

One of my friends grabbed my wrist under the hand dryer in the bathroom one day and just gasped. My PE teacher started to ask me what I was eating for lunch. I specifically remember her telling me, "Marion, your heart is a muscle just like any other muscle in your body. You have to fuel your body or your heart could get too tired and just stop." Everything she said was true, but I was so engrossed in my sickness that I didn't care. Her words went in one ear and out the other. Nothing anyone could say would make everything better.

I distinctly remember one night when I woke up in the middle of the night. Sometimes when that happened, I was scared to go back to sleep because I was afraid that I wouldn't wake up the next morning. But that particular night, while I was waiting to fall back asleep, I got on my computer. Somehow, I ended up on a website that listed symptoms and signs of anorexia nervosa. I read all of them. Everything I was reading matched up with what was going on in my life.

Extreme weight loss and thin appearance. Even though I didn't think I was too thin and hadn't seen how much I weighed since the summer, I knew that I had lost a significant amount of weight and was thinner.

Fatigue. Oh, so maybe that explained why I was tired all the time. Maybe not eating enough was the reason I never had any energy.

Dizziness or fainting. Things were getting to the point where I had to stand up really slow if I had been sitting down or lying down for a while. If I got up too fast, everything went black for a few seconds, and I would feel like I was about to pass out.

Thinning hair. I had always had thick, wavy hair. While my hair was still thick, I had noticed that it had definitely started to fall out.

Absence of menstruation or amenorrhea. While I had never actually started my period before this problem began, everyone else my age had. I was falling behind in terms of normal growth and development.

Development of fine hair on the extremities (lanugo). So THAT is what the "peach fuzz" growing on my body was. It was similar to baby hair, trying to keep me warm.

Constipation. Definitely not going into detail on this one, but let's just say I could relate to this symptom.

Intolerance of cold. This had started back in the summer. I always had to wear a sweatshirt or jacket inside. I was freezing all the time.

Flat mood. Where had my personality gone? I was a shell of the person I had once been.

Excessive exercise. Maybe I didn't see it as obsessive at the time, but coming home to run after I had already been to basketball practice, forcing myself to run even when I didn't want to . . . problem.

Frequent checking the mirror. This was a big one. Every time I took a shower, I had to inspect every part of my body to make sure it was still the same size or smaller than it had been the previous time. Each time I went to the bathroom, I would lift my shirt up to make sure my stomach was still flat.

Eating only a few certain "safe" foods. Well, that was a given, considering I had eaten the same thing for breakfast and lunch almost every day for the past six months.

Difficulty concentrating. For a girl who was always on top of her homework and grades in school, having a hard time focusing was not fun.

Food rituals. I did several things at meal times that were very obsessive-compulsive and abnormal.

Counting calories. I could tell you the exact number of calories in any given amount of food.

Preoccupation with food. Well, I guess that would explain the time spent reading cookbooks and watching Food Network on television.

Withdrawal from usual friends and activities. I couldn't remember the last time I did something fun with a friend.

At that moment, I knew that I had a serious problem and seriously needed help. But part of the problem was that I was too scared to ask for help. I was scared to ask for help because I didn't want to admit that I was struggling with something, but I was also scared to ask for help because that meant that I couldn't continue losing weight. It meant that I would have to start eating more, and start eating a wider variety of foods. That sure wasn't going to happen. I went to another website that was a blog of some sort that gave the daily routine of a girl with anorexia. While I'm not sure if it was a fictional account or someone's own experience, I could relate to almost everything that was written.

I couldn't take it anymore. I closed my laptop and began to silently cry in my bed. I didn't want my parents to hear me crying. I didn't want them to know that their seemingly perfect daughter, the one who made straight A's in school and never got in trouble, was having a hard time. I eventually fell asleep, but from that point on, I felt like I had this dark secret hanging over me. I wanted so badly to tell someone, but this vicious monster that was now inhabiting my brain wouldn't allow it. I had to continue to suffer.

Basketball season that year didn't have a happy ending. The hard work that I willed myself to put in didn't end up reaping any rewards. I was a benchwarmer for 98% of the minutes that our team was on the floor. Sure, I got my chance occasionally. Only if our team was down and had absolutely no chance of catching back up. The only way I would get to play would be if there was no chance of me making things worse than they already were. I was weak. I was easy to steal the ball from. I was easy to play defense on. I wasn't aggressive. And I still couldn't shoot.

Chapter Three

THE CHOCOLATE CHIP COOKIE CAKE

IN DECEMBER, I TURNED FOURTEEN years old. Each birthday prior to this one, I had spent in the company of lots of friends. No matter what kind of birthday party I had, I was always surrounded by my closest friends. But this birthday was different. In a sense, I didn't have any friends anymore. My only friend was my eating disorder.

I spent the day going to a Clemson basketball game with my dad. I had grown up going to Clemson basketball games with my dad, and we always enjoyed spending that time together. We usually went to Chick-fil-A on the way to the game, and then we always had a tradition of getting peanut M&M's on the way to the basketball games and eating them at the game together. There was absolutely no way that I could go to Chick-fil-A. I had to eat the same thing I usually ate at home. I had to measure everything out precisely. And I for sure was not going to eat fast food.

Luckily, we decided to eat lunch at home before the game that day. It was a Sunday, so Chick-fil-A was closed. I didn't have to face that fear. We stopped at a store to get our candy on the way to the game. I eyed the yellow bag of peanut M&M's that I would have previously bought without a question. There was no way I could eat them, but I couldn't just not get candy. I couldn't make it even more obvious than it already was that I had a problem. So, I settled for something that felt a little safer to me . . . pretzel M&M's. They had about 80 calories less.

We finally got to the game. It was fun, but sitting still for that amount of time doing nothing while watching athletes running and jumping and burning calories really got to me. I wanted to be exercising too. Eventually, my dad suggested that we eat our candy. I opened the blue bag of chocolate covered pretzel pieces that I had in my hand. I remember eating those and making them last throughout the whole entire game. Eating them so slowly was partially due to my anxiety about eating them in the first place, but I also hadn't had chocolate in a really long time, and I was determined to make them last.

The game ended, and we drove back home to Greenville. As soon as we got back home, I decided that I needed to go for a run. I had been sitting still for too long, and I needed to burn off the candy calories that I had consumed. I had a little bit of time to go run before we had my birthday dinner, so I put on my fleece-lined leggings and a sweatshirt to go run on that chilly December afternoon when any other person would have wanted to be bundled up in a blanket on the couch inside. And maybe I wanted to be bundled up in a blanket on the couch as well, but I didn't have a choice. I had to do what that little voice in my head was telling me.

"Go run, Marion, you're lazy."

"Go run, Marion, you shouldn't have eaten those M&M's."

"Go run, Marion, don't you want to be perfect?"

"If you don't run today, you're going to gain weight. You're going to wake up fat and out of shape tomorrow."

Like I said, I had no choice. I had to go run. So I headed outside and got my run in for the day before my mind went even foggier than it already was. I had to quiet that mean voice in my head, even if I could only quiet it for a little bit.

My family has a tradition that whenever it is someone's birthday, we go out to that person's favorite restaurant, or my mom will cook their favorite meal at home. In previous years, we went to a Japanese steakhouse or any one of my other favorite restaurants for my birthday dinner. This year, of course, was different. There was no way I could eat food from Kanpai, the Japanese steakhouse that had been my pick in years past, let alone food from any restaurant at all. So the birthday dinner that I chose for year fourteen was sandwiches. Sandwiches made at home. They had to be made at home and by me so that I was in control of what kind of bread was used, how much meat was put on, and what toppings were added. Nothing against people who really like sandwiches because I'm one of those people, but who celebrates a birthday with deli meat and wheat bread?

We ate dinner as a family, and then I got to open my birthday presents. I had asked for a few little things, but the main thing I wanted was a bike. It would give me another way to burn calories without my parents getting suspicious of me running so much now that cross country had ended. To my joy, I received a bike. But the happiness from getting the bike couldn't take away the deep sadness I felt from not having any friends with me to celebrate my birthday. I ended up going up to my room after dinner was over so I could watch TV or get on the computer. I was ready to call it a day and go to sleep.

But much to my dismay, or much to my eating disorder's dismay, the night wasn't over yet.

I heard my mom's voice calling for me to come downstairs. I had no idea what was going on. Had I known what was waiting for me down there, I would have pretended that I was already asleep. I walked back downstairs to find my brother and his girlfriend at the time, who had just made a quick run to the grocery store. They were holding a chocolate chip cookie cake decorated with blue icing. In curly letters in the middle of the cake were the words "Happy Birthday, Marion!"

I wish I had a picture of my face at that moment. I probably looked like I was on the verge of a panic attack or a breakdown. I wasn't happy at all. The old Marion would have been excited to see this dessert. After all, what is a birthday without a cake of some sort? But the Marion with an eating disordered brain was anything but thankful for this kind birthday gesture. I tried to act like I was happy that they got it for me, but it was hard to act happy when I wanted to scream and yell at them. Didn't they know that I couldn't eat that?

I cut a tiny sliver of cookie cake and scraped every bit of icing off. I was already eating sugar in the cake, I didn't need the extra sugar in the icing. I proceeded to take tiny bites of the cake. I ended up finishing the small slice, but I felt like I was going to be sick. A look of concern and worry swept across everyone in my family's face. Where had their daughter gone? Where had their sister gone? Would she ever come back?

I thanked my brother and my family for making my birthday special and went back upstairs. I cried a lot. I'm pretty sure I cried myself to sleep that night. And it wasn't just because of the cookie cake. Sure, that was part of the problem. But eating disorders aren't just about food. The cookie cake was anxiety provoking, but I was also crying for the special time that could have been had with my family if I wasn't entrenched in my disorder, I was crying for birthdays of years past where my smile was genuine, and I was crying for the friends who were probably off having fun without me.

I was at a loss. I didn't know what to do anymore.

I closed my eyes and eventually drifted off to sleep, hoping that maybe some sort of magic would happen and I would wake up the next morning and realize that all of this had been some sort of nightmare. That's what I felt like I was living . . . a nightmare.

Chapter Four

THE DIAGNOSIS

ONE DAY, COMPLETELY OUT OF the blue, my mom came home from Target with a scale. It had become more obvious that something wasn't right, but they thought that it was simply a phase I was going through. They thought it was as a result of being so active with running and basketball. But at this point, they acknowledged that maybe there was something deeper going on. Immediately, I was intrigued by the idea of having this scale in my house. Now I could actually check and see how much progress I was making in terms of losing weight on a daily basis. But before I could go alone into the bathroom to see how much I weighed, my parents got another idea.

They had opened the scale and placed it on the floor in the middle of their bathroom. Now they called me to come in. They told me to step on the scale. I nervously put one foot on, then the other, and closed my eyes. After I figured enough time had gone by for the number to show up on the screen, I opened my eyes. I saw the number, but I don't think I actually realized the problem until I glanced over at my parents. Shock, disbelief, and concern were splashed across their faces. They were at a loss for words.

I looked down at the number again and was filled with two conflicting emotions. I was filled with a sense of accomplishment first. I had worked hard to try to get my body to be "perfect." The days of turning down my old favorite foods had "paid off." I had lost a significant amount of weight. But I was also filled with worry. I didn't want my parents to be upset with me. I also knew that I was at a weight that was very unhealthy for my body. I walked out of the bathroom without saying a word.

A few nights later, my mom and I were in the kitchen. As she was preparing dinner, she told me that I was going to go to the doctor in a few days to talk about nutrition and to make sure my body was working properly. Again, I was filled with two conflicting emotions. First, I was angry because I didn't want help. I wanted to keep losing weight, and I didn't want to have to start eating the foods that I had determined were off-limits. But then I had a wave of relief rush over me. Something was going to change. I wasn't going to be miserable anymore. I even remember wishing that the appointment was the next day, not a few days later. I'm pretty sure the first emotion got the best of me because I broke down crying and saying that everything was fine. Deep down, we all knew that things weren't.

We always had Martin Luther King Day off from school, so that is when my appointment was made. I woke up that morning and got dressed. I pulled on my jeans that didn't fit right anymore and put on a t-shirt that covered up how small I really was. By this point, I knew I didn't look well. I no longer wanted to show off how thin I had gotten. I didn't want people to be concerned with my size. I wanted to make myself look bigger than I was so that my problem would not seem as severe. Then I put on a jacket because not only was it freezing outside, I was freezing whenever I was inside as well. I came downstairs and fixed breakfast for myself. The breakfast I ate was nowhere near enough, and my mom noticed. She started talking to me about how worried she was, and we both ended up in tears.

Once we finally composed ourselves, it was off to the doctor's office. We sat in the waiting room. I was so anxious. I had no idea what to expect. I sat in anticipation, waiting for my name to be called by the nurse. Finally, my name was called. I'm pretty sure I was shaking at this point because I was so nervous.

The nurse took my mom and me back to where the scale was and made me step on. I could tell by the nurse's reaction that she was concerned as well. She recorded my weight and then took us to the room where I would see my doctor. After she took my temperature and did all the nurse stuff, we waited for the doctor. Even more waiting, even more anxiety. It was quiet in the room. My mom and I didn't talk. We both had too much on our minds.

Eventually, my doctor came into the room. He asked how I was, and I didn't know what to say. He then turned to my mom, who spilled everything about the past few months.

"She's not herself, she won't eat her favorite foods, she's lost so much weight, she is always running, she won't do things with her friends anymore . . ."

I remember my mom started crying, which in turn made me start crying as well. My doctor asked me a bunch of questions and lectured me on the dangers of what was going on. He told me all of the things that could happen to my body if I let this continue. He told me that I was no longer allowed to run, and that I needed to gain the weight back. He recommended that I start drinking Ensure, a nutritional drink, and recommended that I start slowly branching out and reintroducing different foods back into my diet. He told me that I had an eating disorder—anorexia nervosa.

Hearing the words *anorexia nervosa* made everything seem more real. They scared me. I didn't want to have those words attached to me, though I had known for a while that I had an eating disorder. I yearned for the days where I had a healthy relationship with food. I wished that I could just press *rewind* on life and go back to the way things were before I was consumed by my disorder. But that's not the way life works. I had to learn how to fight.

We left the doctor's office on the contingency that I would come back each week to get my weight checked. I was referred by my doctor to a therapist. I understood having to come back to get my weight checked to see if I was gaining like I should, but I didn't understand the idea of seeing a therapist. No one I knew saw a therapist. I wasn't "crazy;" I just had problems with food. I didn't realize that what was going on was just as much a mental problem as it was a physical one. I didn't realize that I had a mental illness, not just a simple problem that could be fixed by eating more. But, I was open to the idea of trying it out.

On the way home, my mom called my dad and filled him in on what the doctor had said. Then, we stopped at the grocery store to pick up a few things, including the Ensure, and I was charged with the task of picking out some new foods to try. I ended up getting a sub from the deli to have for lunch that day, something that I hadn't gotten in months. While eating a sandwich from somewhere other than home scared me, I knew I was going to have to start branching out. I also decided that the first food I wanted to try to re-introduce was Goldfish crackers.

I was having a really hard time picking out other foods to try, so my mom did some picking out for me. White bread went into the cart. I hadn't eaten anything but whole wheat in a very long time. The content of my lunchbox was about to start looking very different. Per my doctor's orders, my parents were now going to be in charge of what went into it. I don't remember much of what Mom got for me, but I do remember that I wasn't happy about the new food choices.

While I was nervous, I was also feeling positive about what was to come. I wanted to get better. I wanted to fight. I wanted to be happy again. But I don't think I realized how hard it was going to be.

That night, I followed another one of my doctor's recommendations and started keeping a journal. I would start by keeping track of what I ate that day. Then I would write one positive thing that happened that day in terms of food, and finally I would write about my day in general. My first journal entry showed that while I was scared, I was going to give recovery a try. Here are excerpts from later journal entries that showed I was willing to fight:

> "I tried to eat all of my Goldfish at lunch but I couldn't quite finish, but I almost did!"

> "Thanks to my fantastic mom and dad, I'm going to do great with this recovery. I haven't really thought negatively about it yet because I know it's for my own good, I just hope I can keep away the negative thoughts when I start to gain some weight back."

> "I ate more of my Goldfish today, which made me feel good. I felt like I had more energy today too."

> "I think the best thing right now is that I feel relief, because I think I knew for a while that I had an eating disorder, I just didn't know how to tell anyone or get help because I never imagined that it would happen to me."

> "I just have to stay positive and know in my head that I CAN overcome this."

Even though I was definitely trying to fight my eating disorder and do the things I needed to do to get healthy, I still had a hard time. Recovery isn't something that just happens automatically. All the disordered thoughts don't go away immediately. I wish it worked that way, but it doesn't.

Here are some more excerpts that show I was still having a hard time.

> "I also kind of had a mental breakdown tonight, and I talked to Mom and Dad a lot about it, and I feel better now. I guess I just kind of felt disappointed in myself, knowing that I do have a serious problem."

"I need help to get these 'I'll get fat' and 'I can't eat that' thoughts out of my head."

"I wish things could be the way they used to be."

"It was kind of hard because my head kept telling me that it was way too much food. I was crying a lot. I feel like no one gets how hard it is. I know it sounds simple—just to eat it—but the truth is, it's a lot more difficult than it seems, especially when your head tells you that it is a lot of food. I just wish there was a simpler way of getting rid of this eating disorder. Like I wish I could just snap my fingers and be healthy, but I can't. I feel like everyone is mad at me and is just trying to shove food down my throat. I want things to be like they were before I got this stupid thing called anorexia. I guess I'm just frustrated with myself more than anything for letting it get so out of hand when I knew I had a problem. I just had no idea how to stop it. If I could have any wish right now, it would be to go back in time and start all over again, since I have caused so much pain for everyone. I know I'm not going to get 'fat' by eating, it's just difficult to make myself want to eat big portions or stuff that's fried or cookies or anything like that, and quite frankly I'm not sure how to tell myself that it is perfectly fine to eat those things. I just can't believe that I let myself get like this."

"This morning was awful. It was probably the worst I've felt about this whole thing. But you know, to make a rainbow, you have to have a storm first. I know things aren't going to be easy, but hey, it's life . . . what is easy?"

As you can see, I was still struggling with trying to eat more, with the idea of weight gain, and with feeling guilt and shame from my diagnosis. I was struggling with the strain that my disorder had put on my parents. I was really angry at myself and angry at my eating disorder. But there was still a glimmer of hope somewhere inside me. I wasn't going to simply give up and dive back wholeheartedly into my disorder, as much as I wanted to at times.

After playing phone tag for a few weeks, I eventually ended up seeing the therapist that the doctor referred me to. I saw her twice, but it just wasn't a good fit, so my parents and I decided that I wouldn't see her anymore. There's nothing wrong with not seeing a certain therapist if it isn't a good fit, but what neither I nor my parents realized is that I was truly in need of professional help with my recovery process. We still didn't exactly realize that there was a problem in my head, not just a problem with my physical appearance. Because we didn't realize this, we decided that I wouldn't see a therapist. I would recover on my own with my parents being more in charge of my food and by continuing to have my weight monitored at the doctor's office each week like I had been doing.

After a few weeks of not making a lot of progress, my parents and I had a long heart-to-heart conversation and decided that if I didn't start making the effort and progress that I needed to, we were going to have to look for outside help again. That wasn't something that I wanted to have happen, so I decided to work even harder. The number on the scale started going up each week, and although I grieved a little each time for my "perfect" body that was starting to get bigger, I was excited that I was meeting goals set for me by my doctor. I began to eat a bit more. I was encouraged by the "Great job, Marion!" and "I'm so proud of you!" that I would get after meals.

Things weren't always a walk in the park, but I wasn't as miserable as I had been, and life was coming back into my face.

Chapter Five

MOVING FORWARD

I CONTINUED TO COMPLY MOST of the time with what my parents asked me to eat. I continued to comply with not running. I continued to make upward progress on the scale. I was not only gaining back weight, but I gained energy as well. I had the energy to go hang out with friends with whom I had rekindled relationships. I had energy to go shopping with my mom. I didn't feel like I was going to pass out anymore when I got up to turn something in for one of my classes. I didn't feel dizzy walking down the hallway at my middle school. Things were looking up for me.

Finally, summer came, and I finished middle school. For some people, middle school is great. Sure, it's an awkward phase of life, but it's also a place where you grow a lot. For me, middle school couldn't end soon enough. Had I not been struggling with my eating disorder, things might have been different. But I was ready to move on to bigger and better things.

That summer continued to be full of reintroducing my old favorite foods into my diet and trying to get up to the weight that my doctor had set for me. It wasn't uncommon for my dad and me to go get milkshakes multiple nights during the week. It wasn't uncommon for me to have two bagels at breakfast or two sandwiches at lunch. I was determined to get healthy again, and I was willing to eat things that I wouldn't have touched a few months prior.

My motivation for gaining weight was the fact that once I reached a certain weight, I would be allowed to gradually start running again. Running had been abused by my eating disorder, but deep down I truly loved the sport. Cross country conditioning was starting as soon as school let out, and while I wasn't healthy enough to go right at the beginning, it didn't take long for me to get there. The day my doctor finally cleared me to go back to cross country practice was a day of rejoicing. I was so excited! I started out going only three times a week, but after months of not running at all, that was totally fine with me.

Going back to practice and seeing all of my friends from the team was so much fun. Being able to run and not feel weak was great. Having my coach tell me that he was proud of me was one of the greatest feelings. Cross country helped motivate me to keep on the path of recovery. We had a chance at winning state that year, and I was going to do anything I could to be a part of that. After missing out on the state team the year before—thanks to my eating disorder—I had to redeem myself this year.

I also started my freshman year of high school, and I was loving every minute of it. A fresh start was just what I needed. It was great to meet new friends and get involved in school activities. I had started a new phase of my life and was set on not having my eating disorder take control again.

As the cross country season went on, I was running better than I ever had in my life. I felt strong. I ate enough to sustain the intensity of exercise and the number of miles that I was running. I was eating so that I could run, I wasn't running so that I could eat. I continued to gain a little more weight.

Before I knew it, I was toeing the line at the South Carolina High School League Cross Country State Championships. I remember standing at the starting line with my teammates, in awe of the fact that I was there. After what my life had been like leading up to the last year's state championship, it was a miracle that I was a part of that team.

The gun went off, and all of the runners were on their way through the 3.1 mile cross country course at Sandhills Research Center in Columbia. Each of my teammates knew that they needed to have a good race, and we knew the teams that we needed to pass.

About twenty minutes later, we were done running. We all huddled near the finish line with our coaches. A few loyal cross country dads were frantically trying to do some calculations to figure out what place we might have gotten. Going into the race, we knew that we had a chance at winning, but we had to beat two of the best teams in the state.

If you don't know anything about cross country, you probably have no idea how a team actually wins a meet. It is all scored by points, and the lowest score wins. Seven people usually run in a state championship for each team, with the top five finishers on each team being scored. Each place is a point. So if you had a teammate who finished in first place, that would be one point, second place would be two points, and so on. After some rough calculations were done, it looked like we had come out on top, but we weren't exactly sure.

Finally, it was time for the awards ceremony. Third place was announced. Then second, then first.

Daniel High School, 134 points.

Hilton Head High School, 98 points.

After hearing those two schools announced as third place and second place, we knew that we had won.

Eastside High School, 52 points.

We had done it! All the early morning practices, hard interval workouts, hill repeats, ice baths . . . everything paid off. We were so excited that we even shed some tears. We were state champions!

It was surreal. I couldn't believe it. I was just as excited as the rest of my teammates, but I was also overwhelmed with a sense of joy and pride and accomplishment at what had just happened. I had gone from being sick and underweight and unable to run, to making a comeback and being strong and healthy and a state champion. At that point, I was thankful for recovery and for what it had given me.

We stayed at the meet for a bit to cool down and celebrate with our teammates and families. Then we headed home. Cross country season had ended, and it was time for me to start basketball again.

Basketball during my freshman year went a lot better than basketball did the year before, much like it was with cross country. I had no problem running up and down the court. I was aggressive and could play good defense, and I could make three-pointers again without a problem. I played on the junior varsity team and enjoyed getting to play in all of the games. After sitting on the bench for basically the entire season in 8th grade, I gladly welcomed the playing time that

I got. Things were going great. I was still focused on getting well. I still struggled occasionally with fear of eating certain foods and still struggled a little bit with the way I viewed myself, but compared to the past, things were a million times better.

After basketball ended, I started track season. I made even more improvements in terms of running during this time and was amazed at all of the things my body could do with proper nutrition. I ran times that I never thought I would be able to run.

While my identity was starting to shift more and more away from my eating disorder, it was starting to shift more and more into my identity as a runner. I was becoming known as "Marion the Runner." People would always ask me about running. I planned my entire day around running. Running was my life. But even something good like running can start to become a bad thing.

I went into the summer before sophomore year convinced that I was going to do what I could to make the coming cross country season just as good if not better than the one before. Several of our top runners had graduated, and I had the chance to help lead the team. I felt strong and ran well throughout training that summer. Then my sophomore year started, and the pressure started to hit me. With the top girls having graduated, I put more pressure on myself to perform to the next level. I put expectations on myself, and because of my perfectionistic personality, not reaching those expectations caused me to deem myself a failure.

I started dealing with anxiety about running. I started worrying about practice again, much like I would worry in 8th grade about practice. I started getting anxious about races instead of trusting my body to perform. It was getting to the point where my anxiety was causing physical symptoms such as chest pain and headaches. I wasn't sure what was going on, but I knew something wasn't right. I tried to push through, but things still felt off. I ended up winning our region championship that year and was so happy that I accomplished that. But after that, things started to go downhill, and anxiety took over.

The season came to an end, the state championship was held again, and I ran almost a minute slower than I was supposed to, according to the way our training was planned. I felt awful the whole run. To deal with the anxiety I was feeling, I had started restricting my food intake a little bit toward the end of the season. It wasn't anything drastic like it had been in the past, but considering the amount of running I was doing, it was enough to make me start to feel sluggish. I was just ready for the season to be over. Instead of repeating our title as state champions, we dropped down to fifth place.

Basketball season came around again, but this time I moved up to the varsity team. While I would say that I was a pretty good player on the junior varsity level, moving up to varsity put me right back on the bench. I worked hard in practice but rarely got to play in games. Even though cross country had ended, my anxiety only transferred over to basketball. I was anxious about making a mistake in practice, anxious about getting to play in games, just anxious in general. And as had happened previously, since I wasn't getting to play very much, I felt like I wasn't doing enough exercise, and my food intake started to suffer again.

I didn't feel like myself. I had worked so hard on my recovery. This just felt like I had slid down the mountain all over again.

One day, I finally was able to put into words how I felt. I came home from school crying, went up into our bonus room, and called my dad at work. After I talked to him, he called my mom, who came right upstairs as soon as she got home from work and talked to me for a really long time. A phrase I had been searching for finally came to me. These were the words that finally made everything make sense: "Mom, my body is fine, but my mind isn't." Although I was healthy on the outside, I was still struggling with eating disorder thoughts, and I couldn't handle it on my own anymore.

We decided then and there that I would try to see a different therapist. So I grabbed my laptop and put "eating disorder therapists in Greenville" in the search engine and found several different options. I clicked on a few until I found one that looked like someone I would be able to connect with. My dad agreed to call the next day to set up an appointment. I felt relieved. I had another chance at getting the help I needed. I finally realized that an eating disorder wasn't only a physical problem, not only a problem with my body; it was also a mental illness. And just like with a physical illness where you see a doctor, a mental illness needs to be treated by a professional as well.

Chapter Six

A NEW CREATION

THE FOLLOWING DAY, MY DAD made my appointment with the new therapist. I was excited for the appointment because I truly did want things to be completely better. I didn't want to have just a healthy body but also a healthy mind.

That first appointment came a few days later. I met the therapist and felt that she could really help me. I began seeing her each week and started making small steps toward a healthier mind. Along with seeing her, I saw a dietitian who put me on a meal plan and helped me figure out how to fuel my body properly, because even though I had been eating enough in some phases since my diagnosis, I wasn't consistent with giving my body what it needed.

I was still able to run track during this time, but my coach was aware that I was seeing a therapist and that I would have to miss some practices for appointments. My coach even watched me eat snacks that I was supposed to bring to eat after practice some days. I wasn't able to fully devote myself to training because of appointments after school, so my running suffered. But this time it wasn't suffering because I was ill-nourished; it was suffering because I was devoting my time to something that was more worthwhile for my health. I definitely wasn't going to quit track though, considering I still loved it and loved getting to spend time with my friends on the team.

One day a close friend on the team told me about a retreat for a student-led Bible study group at my school called First Priority. The retreat would be at a place called Camp Greenville. First Priority met on Friday mornings at our high school before the school day started. While I considered myself a Christian, I wouldn't say that my relationship with the Lord was my "first priority" at this time. But for whatever reason, and I can attribute this only to the work of God, I decided on our run that day that I wanted to go on this retreat, even though I had never been to First Priority on a Friday morning in my entire high school career.

After we finished practice, I hurriedly unzipped my book bag and got my phone to text the girl in charge of the retreat. I asked her if it was too late to sign up. Luckily, that day was the very last day, so I still had a chance. I came home from practice, explained it all to my parents, and turned in a check that night. My parents were glad to see me wanting to do something outside of just being at home and running, and I was excited to go on this trip. I had a feeling that it was going to be great. And wow, was I right.

We arrived at the camp for the retreat on a Friday afternoon. The theme of the weekend, and what was going to be taught, was simply "The Gospel." The first night, the speaker started out talking about creation, and how we were all created in the image of God, and created to have peace with God, peace with others, peace with ourselves, and peace with creation. The next morning, he talked about how sin and brokenness entered the world in the Garden of Eden with Adam and Eve. Even though I had been on this retreat for less than twenty-four hours, and nothing drastic had happened, I sensed a feeling of freedom and peace that I hadn't felt in a long time, or maybe ever.

After the session that morning, we went to lunch. I ate a hamburger and an orange, and then I was brave enough to go back to the line after I finished and get some fries like everyone else was eating. That was unlike me. While my list of foods that I would eat had largely expanded, there were still some foods that were fears for me, and french fries were on that list.

But something felt different that day. I spent the afternoon hiking on one of the trails with some friends. Later, I sat at a picnic table with one of my close friends for probably three hours, talking about life and telling her about my struggles.

While the retreat had exceeded all of my expectations thus far, I had no idea what I was in for that night. We went into the third session, a session about God sending Jesus to save us from our sin and brokenness. A session about God sending Jesus to take the punishment that we deserve. A session about being free. After our speaker was finished talking that night, there was a time for thought and response to the powerful message that had just been delivered. A friend of mine started crying, and I had no idea why. I saw a few other people in the room wiping tears from their eyes. I honestly thought it was weird that they were crying. Nothing sad was happening. This was just a cool message. But then, out of nowhere, I started bawling my eyes out, crying really hard. Odd that it happened right after I had just thought that those people crying were crazy. Funny how stuff happens like that, right?

Our speaker had brought out three cinderblocks and a triangular piece of wood and put them in the middle of the room. Each cinderblock had a different word on it. One block said Lord, one block said Savior, and one block said King. These blocks represented making Jesus the Lord, Savior, and King of our lives. Then, the wooden triangle was inscribed with "The Kingdom of God is at hand." He stood the blocks up vertically and then placed the triangle on top to form a platform. He then demonstrated how the platform couldn't stand if any of the three blocks weren't there. The platform couldn't stand with the Lord part missing. The platform couldn't stand with the Savior part missing. And it couldn't stand with the King part missing. All three of those components had to be there.

The speaker then opened up the floor for us to go, as we felt led, and stand on this structure to represent that we were standing firm in our faith that Jesus had come to die for us and that if we trusted Him as our Lord, Savior, and King, we would be able to have eternal life and hope for a future spent with our Father in heaven. Before the speaker sat down, he demonstrated standing on the structure to show that it was stable enough to stand on, because I'm sure I wasn't the only one who was skeptical about standing on three cinderblocks and a piece of wood.

People started going to stand on the structure and, through this simple act, proclaim that they believed in the life, death, and resurrection of Jesus Christ. At this point, I was still in tears. The tears were flowing freely and showed no signs of stopping. But probably three-quarters of the room was in the same situation with tears as I was. The reality of our sin was great, but the idea that Jesus had covered that so we didn't have to pay the price was greater. After thinking and praying, which felt super unfamiliar to me since it wasn't something that I had been regularly doing, I decided to go stand on the cinderblocks.

The worship band was playing music during our chance to respond to the message, and I distinctly remember the song that was playing when I finally went to stand. The song was called "Beautiful Things" by a band called Gungor. The lyrics of the song are truly beautiful, and I would definitely recommend listening to them.

I stood there in that moment, standing in front of classmates, teachers, and friends, and proclaimed through my actions that I was a new creation. I had grown up going to church and grown up thinking that I was a Christian. I had recently started going to youth group with several of my friends from school. But after hearing the gospel presented in its entirety that weekend, I had a new understanding of what having a relationship with Jesus actually meant. So while this song was playing in the background, I prayed on that platform for God to help me to be free of my disorder. I prayed for Him to help me trust in Him and in Him alone. And I stepped down feeling like a weight had been lifted. I felt like a completely new person, which in a way, I was a new person. Second Corinthians 5:17 (ESV) states, "Therefore, if anyone is in Christ, he is a new creation. The old has passed away; behold, the new has come." I was born again. Made new. Redeemed. Set free. A new Marion.

That was probably the most beautiful feeling I have ever experienced. I was smothered with hugs from some of my closest friends who were on the retreat with me. I smothered them back in hugs as well when they stepped off of the platform whether they had given their life to Jesus for the first time or were simply demonstrating that they still firmly believed in Him as their Lord, Savior, and King.

On our hike earlier that day, we had been instructed by our speaker to pick up a rock and carry it with us all day. We had no idea why we were supposed to do that, but each of us did. So after the response part of the night was over, we were instructed to get our rocks. We were told how carrying around those rocks all day was like how we have to carry around all our sin and struggles. We were to go get the rock, pretend that it was a specific struggle we were dealing with, take it outside, and chuck it into the lake at Camp Greenville. I threw that rock, representing my eating disorder, as hard and as far as I could into the depths of the water in that lake. It was such a tangible way of demonstrating what had just happened to me spiritually. The burdens I had been carrying myself for so long, like the rock I had been carrying around all day, were no longer mine to carry. I was free because of what was done for me on the cross so long ago.

After everyone re-entered the room where we had our sessions, it was time for a celebration. It was time for a dance party. So with music blaring, we danced and laughed into the wee hours of the morning.

Later, it was time for us to return to our cabins. Some of the girls in my cabin decided they were going to wake up early the next morning to see the sunrise at a lookout point at Camp Greenville that is appropriately named Pretty Place. We woke up the next morning, about three hours after we went to sleep, and made the trek to Pretty Place to watch the sunrise. It was breathtaking and worth the lack of sleep.

I woke up feeling genuinely happy that morning. I didn't feel like I had to fake my smile or fake my happiness. It flowed out of me freely. I was full of joy, and I knew it. At breakfast, I ate pancakes, bacon, eggs, and yogurt with granola without a second thought. I enjoyed it instead of trying to calculate the calories in my head.

I went home that weekend with a new outlook on life. For several weeks after getting home from the retreat, I was riding a "spiritual wave," I guess you could say. But just because I became a Christian on that retreat didn't mean that my problems were going to be magically gone, contrary to what I thought. I was still going to have to fight. I did continue to fight for that freedom for those weeks that I was "riding that wave." Then, on the evening of Thursday, April 18, 2013, at the county track meet, my wave crashed.

Chapter Seven

THE INJURY

IT WAS THE FIRST DAY of the Greenville County Track and Field Championships. The track meet where every high school in Greenville County came out to run. The meet was hosted by Eastside, my high school. All week leading up to the meet, I had been excited but nervous. I knew that this meet wasn't the most important meet out of the entire season; state qualifiers and the state championship were what I needed to set my focus on. But after I had missed several meets already that season and had continued to miss practice due to therapy and nutrition appointments, I felt like I needed to prove myself. I was scheduled to run the 3200, which is just about two miles. The 3200 was my favorite event, and the event for which I had gone to state the previous track season. It wasn't anything I hadn't done before. Just eight laps around the track, that was all. The meet started at 5:00 pm, and all of the events were spread over two days, Thursday and Friday. My event was scheduled to be one of the last events on Thursday, around 8:00 that night.

After school, I went out to the track and helped my team get the track ready, then waited with my teammates until it was time to run our races. The afternoon was spent sitting in the bleachers, eating granola bars and bananas, cheering on teammates in other races, and anxiously waiting until time to warmup. Only two of us from Eastside were running the 3200, myself and one of my close friends on the team.

It finally came time for us to warm up, so we headed out on a short run to loosen up our muscles. We waited on the back field, checked in and got our hip numbers, and then went onto the infield to wait to be called onto the track. Soon enough, we were standing on the line, hearing the words, "Ladies, there will be two commands. Runners on your mark, then the gun." We stood on the line and were instructed to take a step back, like usual. Once the starter said, "Runners on your mark," we came up to the actual starting line. When we heard those words, we all stepped up to the line and stood ready, anticipating the sound of the starting gun. The gun went off, there were simultaneous beeps of watches starting, and we were off.

The first three and a half laps were great. Almost a mile had gone by, and my teammate and I were running together, pushing each other. However, once I got to the 200 meter mark on my fourth lap, with a half a lap to go until my first mile of the two mile race was complete, I noticed something. My shoe had come untied.

I could have sworn that I double knotted my racing flats right when I put them on, but I guess I hadn't. Either that or my shoelaces were doing something crazy while I was running! I wasn't sure what to do in that situation. Since I was in the middle of a race and running well, I didn't want to stop and tie it. I figured it wouldn't be too hard to run the rest of the race with my shoelace flopping around. I tried to just ignore it and ran the rest of that lap.

Once I came through the line, ready to start my fifth lap, I decided that I was going to speed up. I was feeling great, the weather was great, and I knew I was capable of running faster than I was. However, once I got to the first turn on that lap and sped up, the shoe lace that was untied somehow got tangled up with my other shoe. Next thing I knew, I was going down.

At that time, our track was still asphalt. Most high school tracks are rubber now, which would have been helpful with the scenario that was about to occur. I went down on the ground, left knee first.

As soon as it happened, I didn't think much of it. I thought I had simply tripped, and I thought I could get right back up and finish running. Sure, I might have a scrape on my knee, but I could push through. I reached beside me to push my body back up off the ground and get back up, but I couldn't get up. Stunned, I didn't know what to do, and I needed to get out of the way of other runners quickly. I eventually rolled or scooted off the track into the field. At that point, my eyes started welling up with tears. I was hurting. It wasn't just a scrape. Through the foggy tears in my eyes, I saw my dad running from one side of the fence onto the track to come to me. I heard over the loud speakers, "We need an Eastside coach at the first turn." Our athletic trainer drove across the field in his Gator tractor. I had my coach, my dad, the trainer, and probably a few more people that I don't remember standing over me and looking at my knee.

I didn't want to look at my knee because I didn't want to know the severity of what had happened. I don't do well with blood or swelling or bruises or anything of that nature. From what I heard, however, my knee had already started bruising and was pretty swollen. I had hit the ground really hard, and there was quite a bit of blood.

The athletic trainer started cleaning it off and wanted to find out if I could move it. While it was painful, I could still move my leg without a ton of trouble. He checked it out some more and then wrapped it up with a giant ice pack. Once I caught my breath and stopped crying, my dad and coach helped me stand up, and I hobbled across the track and up into the bleachers where the rest of my team sat. Everyone who was sitting up there, and the rest of Greenville County that was there, saw what had happened. How embarrassing! But no one laughed at me. Everyone wanted to make sure I was all right.

By then, I thought everything was going to be fine. Sure, I was upset that I didn't get to finish the race, but it wasn't the end of the world. Although I was limping, I could move around. No big deal! But, boy, was I in for something unexpected.

I got home that night and realized I was in more pain than I thought. I downed some pain relievers before getting in bed. I situated myself with another ice pack and propped my knee up on a pillow to help with the swelling.

The next morning, the bruising had gotten worse, the swelling hadn't gone down very much, and I was still in pain. I made it to school and limped around all day. Not fun. That weekend, I was still limping and in pain, but my parents and I decided to give it another day or two. By the end of the school day on Monday, I was in tears again. Partially in tears because of how much it hurt, but partially because I knew this wasn't a small bump from a little trip on the track. It was something more. I went by my coach's classroom and told him that I wouldn't be at practice that afternoon because my dad was going to take me to the sports clinic to have my knee examined.

Soon enough, we were in the waiting room of Steadman Hawkins Sports Clinic during their after-hours time. After about an hour and a half of waiting, I was taken back for an x-ray. I remember it being hard for the x-ray technician to get the picture taken because I couldn't straighten out my leg all the way on the table, but after some pulling and prying of my leg, we got it. I was then taken back to a doctor's office, where we waited for the orthopedic doctor to come in and deliver the results.

The doctor came in shortly after and confirmed what I thought might be the case. My patella, otherwise known as my kneecap, was fractured. Thankfully it wasn't a terrible fracture, and my bone hadn't shattered from the impact with the asphalt, but a fracture is a fracture. I broke my kneecap. All because my shoelace came untied. Sure, my bones could have been fragile as a result of the stress I had been putting on my body through my eating disorder. Bones can weaken, and osteopenia and osteoporosis can occur, especially in the event of amenorrhea (lack of a period), like I had experienced. There is no way for me to know if my bones were weakened or if I would have still fractured my kneecap, but it is something important to consider. Still, if the shoelace had not come untied, the fracture would not have occurred.

Obviously, since my kneecap was broken, running was out of the question for a while . . . a few months even. I got my very own knee brace and a set of shiny new crutches. I left the doctor's office that day extremely disappointed. My track season had come to an abrupt end. Running at the regional meet was out of the question. So was running at state qualifiers. And of course, running at the state championship meet was off the table as well. Gone were the days of being at practice every day after school. Instead of getting my workout in at practice, I was getting my workout by hobbling around Eastside High School on crutches with a backpack. That is definitely not an easy task.

Initially, I was hit with disappointment. I was disappointed at the way my season ended. But then, other emotions came. I was angry. If my coach hadn't made me run the 3200. If I had been wearing different shoes. If I had triple-checked to make sure my shoes were tied tightly. If I had actually stopped to tie my shoe when I first noticed that it was untied. If our track had been rubber and not asphalt.

There were so many "ifs" that went through my mind, but I eventually had to realize that I couldn't go back and change what happened. I became extremely anxious. I was anxious about being unable to work out for a good while. The last time I had taken that long off from exercise was when I was in the process of gaining weight. Here I was with the weight all gained back, and I didn't have a way of burning calories. I was terrified that I would gain a bunch more weight. Looking back, feeling this way should have been a huge red flag to me that something was still off in my mind and mental state.

Having to come home from school in the afternoons and take it easy was hard for me. It was hard to pass my teammates who were headed to track practice after school while I was headed home to sit on the couch. But I firmly believe that God always has a plan for everything that happens in our lives. He has a reason for *everything*. And because of the thoughts I had in my mind regarding weight gain and exercise, one of the best things that could have happened to me was my injury. I had made running an idol, and that had been ripped away. I was forced to confront my obsessive exercise tendencies, and

I was forced to eat foods that I usually wouldn't have been comfortable with eating unless I had exercised. I was struggling still with the mindset of using exercise to "earn" food. Exercise shouldn't be used as a way to "earn" food. You get to eat regardless of the amount of calories that you burn off!

While this point in my life was hard, dealing both with the injury and confronting parts of my eating disorder that I otherwise wouldn't have seen, I'm really thankful for my injury and the healing that came from it. Eventually, I got used to the new lifestyle of not being as active, and I realized that not exercising and still enjoying food wasn't going to make me blow up like a balloon. My body was smarter than I thought it was. I just needed to trust it.

I got involved in new hobbies and activities such as painting and writing, took time to hang out with friends more, and held onto the hope that it wouldn't be long before I was able to get back to running. Ultimately, hope got me through the injury.

By the end of June, I was able to start running again. Of course, I had to build back up slowly. Running was extremely hard at first. Since I hadn't done any cardio workouts in a while, I was soon out of breath. I was discouraged that I wasn't able to run like I did prior to the injury. But I had to keep reminding myself that I was just getting back into it, and like anything that you haven't done in a while, it may take time to readjust to doing it again.

However, things during that summer didn't line up in my favor. After running consistently for about two weeks, I went on a mission trip with my youth group and wasn't able to run for about a week. Then, I returned home and had my wisdom teeth removed. That pushed running back even more. Once I was able to run again, I tripped over something in my garage and bruised my shin. Then my junior year of school started, and I sprained my toe. Every worst case scenario situation that could have happened was happening to me. I felt like I hadn't made any progress in terms of getting back in shape, and I was definitely nervous about the cross country season.

I had lofty goals for myself, and I was determined to achieve them. Another perfectionistic quality that can be a blessing and a curse. I had dreams of repeating my title of region champion from the year before. But after the first time trial at practice that season, I had doubts that I would be able to do anything spectacular, let alone even run on the varsity team. The first few meets, I didn't even get to run. When I finally got to run, I was fighting hard for a varsity spot but kept coming up short. It didn't help that practices were still being missed because of therapy and nutrition appointments.

When it finally came time for the state team to be determined, I still had a shot. Like I mentioned in a previous chapter, seven team members run in the state championship. But an eighth runner is also part of the team as an alternate. There were three girls on the team who were close in time, and our coach needed to determine which one of us was going to fill the eighth spot.

So, we all ran in a 5k race. Whoever finished first would get the spot. Fair enough. But deep in my mind, I knew that if I didn't get that spot, I was going to be devastated. Looking back at a journal entry from the night before the race, this is what I wrote:

> "Cross country is honestly what is keeping me from relapsing right now, and if I don't get my spot and my season ends tomorrow, who knows what will happen."

On an October Saturday morning, we lined up at the starting line as we had many times before. The starting gun went off, and we took off running. We all stayed pretty close for the first mile or so but then started spreading apart. One girl was ahead of me, one behind. I had my sights set on the one that I needed to catch. I knew that I needed to keep my pace or speed up to avoid being passed. In the last half mile or so, I could see the girl who was ahead of me, but she started speeding up, while I had nothing left in the tank. She finished first and was awarded the alternate spot on the state team.

I was definitely upset and disappointed, but I was also happy for my teammate. I wasn't raised to be a bad sport, so I congratulated her and realized that maybe it just wasn't meant to be. But on the other hand, I was secretly happy because it meant that I had given myself permission to relapse. If I wasn't running anymore, I didn't think I deserved the calories. It was almost a way of punishing myself for failing.

Chapter Eight

WHO AM I?

MY EATING DISORDER HAD GIVEN me a sense of identity in the past. When I gained back all the weight that I lost, I gave up the identity that came with my eating disorder. But I simply found other things to put my identity in. Running became where my identity was found. First, I had been Marion, the girl with the eating disorder. Then, I was Marion, the runner. I found my identity in these things because it was what I was "good at" during those times in my life.

So, after I failed to get a spot on the state team, I told myself that I was no longer good at running. I was no longer going to be known as "Marion the runner" because I couldn't even make the state team. I decided not to run track that year. I needed a break from running competitively. It was embarrassing for me to be unable to compete like I used to. I couldn't run as fast or as far as I had in the past.

I decided it was time for me to become good at something else. Immediately, the thing I wanted to be good at again was my eating disorder. I wish I had reminded myself that my identity was found in something far greater than my eating disorder and far greater than running. My identity was found in Christ. Deep down I knew that, but it still didn't stop me from moving full speed back toward the illness that had taken so much from me already.

It sounds so twisted for someone to want to be "good at" having an eating disorder. And, yes, it is twisted. But eating disorders aren't rational. They make you think things that you would never think otherwise. Things that a normal person would think are crazy, for lack of a better word. If someone was sick with any other illness, they wouldn't wish to be good at having that illness. They wouldn't wish to be the sickest person with that disease. They would want to get better and would fight with every fiber of their being in order to get better. But sadly, oftentimes eating disorders don't work that way. It becomes a place to find identity and pride yourself in being able to resist cupcakes and ice cream and french fries, a place to fill yourself with a sense of accomplishment when the number dips lower and lower on the scale.

My eating disorder came back in full force, and I did nothing to stop it. My school lunch became smaller and smaller. I would find ways to avoid eating dinner with my family. My energy levels started to fall. I was starting to feel the effects of restricting again, but I had to make everything seem like it was fine. I had to put on a smile, laugh with my friends, and be the normal Marion that my parents were used to. But on the inside, I was starting to unravel.

I had pretended for so long that things were going well. My parents were paying a lot of money for me to go to therapy and nutrition appointments, so I felt like I needed to make them think that everything was significantly improving. If I started doing things that resembled the "pre-eating disorder Marion," I would get affirmation and make my parents proud. But in reality, things were not getting better.

I became good at faking progress and hiding my struggle. Things were getting out of control, but I had already snowballed myself into a big lie, and I couldn't find the strength to admit what was happening. My parents would have been willing to do whatever they could to help me if I'd simply told them what was going on. But since I hadn't told them anything, they were completely in the dark.

Prom season came, and it became a goal for me to look good in my prom dress. Everywhere I turned, I heard girls chatting about how they were going to go to the gym to work out to lose weight for prom. Girls at lunch would be eating a salad because they were on a "prom diet." It took all I had in me not to join the discussions that people were having about weight loss, working out, and calorie counting. I never outwardly told anyone that I wanted to lose weight for prom, but inside my head, I was concocting numerous ways to have the perfect body in a matter of just a few weeks.

I'm pretty sure that during this time, depression started to hit me. I lost interest in things that I had enjoyed before. I wanted to lie around and do nothing all the time. This was hard though. When you have an eating disorder telling you to go workout so that you can burn calories, along with depression that is taking away all of your motivation, you have a war going on in your head. Sure, I would go to the gym occasionally. Or maybe go for a short run during this time. But my answer for this clashing of ideas in my head about what to do was to just eat less. It would appease my depression by not causing me to have to over-exert myself with exercise, and it would appease my eating disorder by causing fewer calories to enter my body.

The day of prom finally came, and I knew I hadn't lost much weight. I didn't like how I looked in my dress. I still had a great time at prom regardless and tried to not let all those negative thoughts about myself take up the time that could be spent enjoying prom. However, the day after prom, I began to look through prom pictures that I had been tagged in on Facebook and prom pictures that I had taken on my phone. I was mortified. I looked at the pictures and was probably the unhappiest I had ever been with my body. To me, my face looked chubby. My arms looked fat. I compared myself to friends I was in pictures with who were smaller than me. I wished I could have looked like them.

Despite how beautiful everyone told me I had looked that night, I couldn't see it myself. Those pictures were all saved on my phone. Looking at them multiple times a day fueled my desire to keep falling deeper and deeper into my relapse. A picture of myself and the boy I went to prom with became my phone's lock screen background. Not because I liked the picture but because I wanted to see that picture each time I looked at my phone. I wanted to be reminded of what I didn't want to look like anymore.

Restriction continued, school finally ended, and summer began. I had decided that I would try cross country again and hopefully get back to where I had been before. I wanted to redeem myself from the previous season. So I started running again, but when you're not giving your body adequate fuel, running becomes difficult. And it was easy for me to get discouraged by that. Even though I was running, eating less, and starting to lose a little weight, I still hated myself. I weighed myself every so often at the home of a family I babysat for, and that number would determine how I felt about myself that day. The number wasn't high by any means, and I was nowhere near overweight. But it was hard for me to see that number and think back to what the number on the scale had said at my lowest weight. I felt like I had let myself get out of control, like I had "let myself go." Journal entries during this time were written like this:

"Stretch marks. Lovely."

"I have to go to a pool party for church tomorrow night. It's not going to be terrible because I am wearing a one piece, but still . . . I feel huge."

"I can't stop thinking about the difference in weight between my lowest and now. I feel like my arms are huge. I just want to be skinny again. I miss it."

"I'm just tired of being tired."

Other journal entries showed that I knew that what I was doing was wrong, and part of me didn't want to have to deal with my eating disorder anymore, but the other part of me was so unhappy with my body and how other things in my life were going that I wasn't willing to do anything I needed to do to get better. I wasn't willing to accept my body the way it was, and I wasn't able to see myself for anything other than a number or the various parts of my body that I felt were too big.

I would have a few days here and there where things would be going well, and then I would fall back into the eating disorder even harder. It was the epitome of two steps forward, three steps back. I would make progress . . . I wouldn't weigh myself while I was baby-sitting, I would have a positive thought about my body, I would eat the amount of food that I needed to . . . but then all the progress would be overshadowed by the disordered thoughts and behaviors that would come after.

I was super involved in my church youth group during this time, so I was being poured into and loved on by staff members and interns that summer. I was reminded of truth, but I felt like a fraud. I knew so much of what they were telling me in my head. I knew that I was fearfully and wonderfully made. I knew that my outer appearance wasn't what mattered. I knew that me trying to destroy my body hurt God. I knew that I couldn't be the woman He wanted me to be while tied down to my disorder. I knew that I needed to surrender control. I knew so many things . . . but knowing something and actually believing and doing it are two very different things. I prayed a lot that summer, writing down all my prayers in a journal. I prayed for God to take away my eating disorder, but I didn't mean it. It was just something to say, something for me to tell friends who knew what I was struggling with to convince them I was trying to do something about it.

Around the beginning of July, a random thought that was recovery-focused, but maybe in hindsight was not the right decision for me, popped into my head. Maybe I needed to quit cross country. Maybe the fact that I had broken my kneecap sophomore year and then not performed that well junior year were signs from God that I needed to quit.

I don't think that was actually the case, as cross country was still something that I did enjoy deep down—when it was done in the right way and in a healthy way. But lo and behold, I decided that I was going to quit cross country. No more. I was done. I quit cross country, reasoning that running would cause me to slip even further into my eating disorder and that it added too much stress and pressure on me. But I think the real reason was that if I wanted to run and be good at it, I actually had to eat. I didn't want to eat. I didn't want to feel awful running because I wasn't eating enough. Therefore, the logical thing to do (in my mind) was to quit cross country and cover it up with the fact that I was "doing what I felt like God was telling me to do."

Quitting cross country made the relapse worse. Food became "optional but highly discouraged" in my mind. If I did eat something, it soon came back up through the means of me making myself throw up. That would happen anywhere from one to five times a day, depending on the number of times I would actually eat something. Purging was something that hadn't been a problem when I struggled in the past. It was something that I had tried once or twice but never really saw the point. But this time was different, and it became addictive from the first time it happened. It became a way to punish myself for eating, yet it also gave me a sense of happiness from having the feeling of being "empty" afterwards. (Side note: I later learned that purging doesn't rid you of a significant amount of calories at all. Your body is smart. It absorbs the calories that you eat quickly. Purging basically only has the effect of making your throat hurt, making your hands raw, and can eventually cause more health problems and even death.)

I told only one person about what was happening with making myself throw up. She had been through an eating disorder herself and gave me a stern "talking-to" in a very loving way about why it wasn't good to engage in that behavior and why I needed to stop. I loved her to death and still do . . . she was one of my biggest "recovery role models" and like a big sister to me. But while I definitely respected everything she said, it didn't make a difference because of the state of mind I was in with my eating disorder. Talking to her about it helped though. She taught me ways that I could avoid purging, but those coping skills came in handy only about 25% of the time. I couldn't stop completely.

A few weeks after the purging started, I was supposed to go on a mission trip with my youth group. I was excited about going but also nervous about the food aspect. I wouldn't be able to get away with my new behavior. I was told by one of my youth leaders that if I couldn't make things work on the trip, I would have to be sent home. That in itself was enough to keep me from purging on the trip, because being sent home would be embarrassing and would cause my parents to find out what had been going on. I had been doing a good job of making it seem like everything was perfectly fine and had been able to hide what I was doing in the bathroom. Looking back, while it meant a lot to me that I could trust my youth leaders with what I was going through, there came a point where telling my parents could have been helpful in getting me on the road to recovery sooner.

Because I didn't want to blow my cover with my parents, I decided that I wouldn't make myself throw up on the trip; I would just restrict. Several friends, youth leaders, and interns on the trip knew what was going on, and it was great to have their support and encouragement if I needed it while I was there, because it wasn't easy. But I made it through the trip. I was pretty much in a bad mood the entire trip and wanted to cry at any given moment, but I made it through without having to come home, and that was my goal.

Some of my entries in my prayer journal from the trip said these things:

"Dear God, eating disorders suck. The fact that I am so consumed with wanting to be skinny sucks. But God, right now I don't hate it enough to fully give it over to you, and I know that isn't ok, but there's a disconnect between what I know and my actions. I just don't know what to do. Life is hard. HELP!"

As I mentioned previously, I knew what I needed to do, but I didn't want to do it.

"Dear God, I am a mess. I don't know how much longer I can handle all of this. I'm exhausted. I'm sad. I'm hungry. I feel defeated. I broke down earlier. I lost it. First, the eating here is fueling my ED (eating disorder), and I can't wait to see how much weight I've lost here. I feel so fat. My thighs are huge. I just want to be skinny again. I know it won't satisfy like you will, but I do feel like I will at least feel better about myself. Second, I'm irritated with everything. I already snapped at Joy when she asked if I ate breakfast. I want to go back to sleep. I have no energy. My head hurts. And I need you to hold me because I can't stand on my own feet right now."

What I was doing to myself was really starting to take a toll.

"Dear God, I know I need to eat more because I am literally running on fumes. I have no energy. I know I need to eat more, but I really just don't want to. God, I know you made my body the way it is for a reason, but why? Why did you make me this way? I don't understand."

"Dear God, we went to get ice cream. I freaked out. I ended up getting chocolate with Oreos. Then I started crying. So Cecily went to get MK, and I proceeded to sob even harder, but MK and I talked and she encouraged me, and I eventually ate it. It was hard and I regretted it, but I ate it and kept it down."

Eating disorders make normal, fun events like getting ice cream a huge ordeal. Eating disorders cause secrets to be kept. Eating disorders wear you out, not just from the lack of nutrition entering your body but also from the time and energy exerted in trying to cover your tracks. My eating disorder was a quest for perfection. What I wish I had known, however, is that perfection is unattainable. If I was constantly trying to measure up on the scale of perfection I had created for myself, I would continually fall short.

Chapter Nine

ROCK BOTTOM

AFTER RETURNING TO GREENVILLE, EVERYTHING hit me all at once. The effects of working hard on the trip that week in terms of physical labor as well as being challenged spiritually when I was not in a good place with the Lord were exhausting. Everything I had been going through was piling up on me. Nothing had changed about my mental state. If anything, everything was worse. The day after getting back from the mission trip, I slept almost all day. In my journal that night, I wrote words that I didn't think would ever cross my mind, and things escalated from there.

> "I don't know what to do. And honestly there are thoughts of not wanting to be here anymore, and that scares me a lot."

I was on my way to nowhere fast. I was slipping faster than I ever thought I could slip. I was scaring myself. But I still couldn't stop. I had lost weight. But it still wasn't enough.

> "Dear God, Things are getting worse. This is out of control. I couldn't fall asleep last night, and I cried a lot. I tried to scratch myself pretty hard."

Finally, after an entire week of me moping around the house and doing nothing, my parents figured out that something was up. For a few days, they attributed my actions—or lack thereof—to being extremely tired from the trip. They thought my behavior was normal. But after I consistently moped around the house for more than just a few days, they realized that I wasn't myself. They saw that I wasn't eating. And we talked.

> "Dear God, so a lot has happened in the past few days. I ended up talking to Mom and Dad about mostly everything, which was good that things finally got out to them. It was so hard but I'm glad it happened. Ok so I'm still restricting. I've tried to purge. I have suicidal thoughts. So life's rough. But I had an appointment at The Riley Center, and it was good. I met with a nurse and then the dietitian. Then I met with a therapist, and they decided that I am going to do what is called PHP. So hopefully that will help."

On August 1, 2014, I started treatment at The Riley Center. I was placed in a program called PHP, which stood for Partial Hospitalization Program. I would be there from 8:30-3:30 each day, excluding the weekends. They would weigh me (blindly of course), my vitals would be taken, and I would have breakfast, morning snack, lunch, and afternoon snack there along with numerous therapy groups and individual therapy sessions throughout the day.

I had been in therapy before, but this was like therapy on steroids. Compared to seeing a therapist and dietitian once a week, being in treatment every day for multiple hours was an adjustment. I struggled a lot with the fact that I was required to start eating more and healing. I was mad at myself for not letting myself get skinnier or sicker. I didn't feel like I was as "good" at my eating disorder as I had been previously because I hadn't lost as much weight. But eating disorders are about a lot more than just weight. Though I was mad at myself for not being "better" at my eating disorder, I was also relieved that I was going to get help and that my parents were more in the loop as to what was going on. While I was still keeping secrets, lines of communication were generally more open. I didn't feel the need to keep up my "perfect daughter" façade anymore. I realized the pressure to be perfect was me projecting the idea of perfection onto my parents, not them telling me that I had to be perfect.

Despite being in treatment Monday through Friday, the weekends were still hard. Dinners at home were still hard. My parents were aware of a lot at this time, but they still weren't aware that I was purging. My therapist wanted to put the responsibility on me to admit what I was doing to my parents. But I wasn't able to muster up the courage to talk to them about it. Purging was something that I wasn't willing to do away with. I still was able to use that to cope with the increase in the amount of food I was eating and was able to use that as a way to cope with stress. My parents also didn't realize the extent of my depression and suicidal thoughts at that time, and I don't think I or any of my treatment team realized it either.

I felt like living was a chore. I would wake up, be forced to fill my body with calories that I didn't want to eat, have to talk about how I was feeling, then go to bed and wake up and do it all over again.

By the time school started, I was moved down to a less intense program called IOP (Intensive Outpatient Program) that was in the afternoons/evenings a few days a week. I had made some progress, and it was important for my mental state that I start my senior year of high school on time.

Senior year started out differently than any other year of high school had. I felt disconnected from my friends. Even though I was taking only four classes, I felt overwhelmed. Instead of going to cross country practice after school, I was going to the treatment center for IOP. My friends were getting excited for college applications, but it was still up in the air whether or not I'd get to go to college the following year. If I couldn't function normally at home with my parents there, what would make them think that I would be able to function on my own the following fall?

I was getting even more depressed. I wasn't seeing any progress.

"I feel really low and defeated. I feel hopeless and like I'm never going to recover. I'm not really seeing how it's possible. Kathryn and Mom and Dad say that I've made progress, but I don't see what they're talking about. Sure, I'm eating my meal plan and I haven't purged in a week, but I feel awful. I feel like I'm so fat and all I want to do is get skinny again. I miss when I was smaller. I know I wasn't happy then, but I'm not happy now either. So why not be skinny and unhappy rather than fat and unhappy if I'm going to be miserable either way? I feel alone. At school, I am surrounded by people and still feel alone. I have to blink back tears all day, and then when I'm finally by myself, I can cry. In the shower. In my bed. Then I just sleep to escape. I don't want to do this anymore. Recovery seems impossible. And if I'm going to keep feeling this way, then what's the point of even being alive? I feel worthless, frustrated, overwhelmed, uncertain, worried. I just want to escape. I NEED HELP."

After feeling like this for weeks upon weeks, even with individual counseling and nutrition appointments and the IOP program, I was sure that nothing would ever get better. This feeling went on and on. Feelings of hating myself and not feeling worthy of recovery or even life plagued me. After eight weeks in IOP, insurance decided to no longer pay for my treatment, and I "graduated." I was going to see my therapist and dietitian weekly at this point.

I still had no intentions of things ever getting better. I didn't believe that things ever could get better, and so I wrote, "Recovery is never really going to happen . . . I'm just going to be stuck in this whole up and down situation, acting like things are ok because they should be, beating myself up, wanting to go back to my ED be-really-skinny-again mindset forever."

Things at home were tense. There were multiple arguments during the day about what I was or wasn't eating. I was mean. I said things I shouldn't have. I threw temper tantrums when my parents would make me eat certain things. Many tears were shed by everyone. I felt like I had disappointed my parents and screwed my family up. I felt guilty for bringing up the fact that I was struggling again back during the summer. If only I had hidden it better, everything would be fine. Of course that was a lie that I told myself, but it seemed like it was true.

I remember Sunday night, October 19, 2014, vividly. I couldn't sleep, so I pulled out my prayer journal and began to write. I hadn't written in this journal for two months. Looking back at my journal, it's evident that I was in a panic when writing. My neat, small, delicate handwriting on the pages before contrasts heavily with the rushed, large, messier handwriting that spread across the next few pages. There are marks on the page where I can see crinkles from teardrops hitting the paper and smearing the pencil I was writing with. I was at the end of my rope, and the only thing I could think to do was pray.

The entire journal entry spreads over four notebook-paper sized pages. The general premise of the journal entry was me listing out ten reasons why I didn't want to recover and why I didn't think recovery was possible. I explained each of the reasons in great detail. But then the journal entry took a turn that even I didn't see coming when I was writing it.

"I do realize that you have so much for me ahead, that you love me, and that you created me beautifully in your image. But for some reason, there's a disconnect between my head and my heart. And even though I know these things, I don't feel like anything is changing. It's like I know 2+2=4, but that doesn't change me in any way. I just feel so stuck. God, I'm not really sure where to go from here or what to do. Sometimes (a lot) I think things would be so much better if I wasn't here anymore. If I was just gone and didn't have to deal with my ED, depression, anxiety . . . anything. I've seriously thought through ways to do it. 'Accidentally' take too much medicine. 'Accidentally' get in a wreck or run my car off the road. Somehow end up with something around my neck. And I'm scared. I don't feel safe. I don't trust myself. Life is really hard. Sure, there are a few good moments every once in a while, and I am thankful for those, but I can't keep doing this much longer. I don't know what needs to happen, what I need to do, what you have planned, but all I know is that I need you to do something quickly and I need help. Please God, I'm begging and pleading with you. I can't keep doing this. Help. Sometimes I wish I was dead so I didn't have to look at myself every day, didn't have to deal with all of this, just didn't have to feel anything. I just feel hopeless. At a loss. Defeated."

Eventually that night, I fell asleep. I woke up for school and came downstairs like normal. I ate breakfast. I went to school. I'm pretty sure I was in a daze all day at school. I was there physically, but mentally, I was gone. I had a lot on my mind. I came home from school. I ate lunch. I went to therapy. It is truly a blessing that I had an appointment with my therapist scheduled for that day.

I spent probably the first thirty minutes of the hour-long session trying to avoid talking about the journal entry. We talked about other things that I pretended were really important, but looking back they were extremely trivial compared to what I really needed to share. I knew I wouldn't be able to tell my therapist verbally what I needed to, so I brought my journal with me. When we had about ten minutes left, I pulled out the journal and just handed it to her and told her to read it. She did. I cried. A lot. We talked about what needed to happen. She told me that she was going to call my mom. She asked if I was safe to drive home. I reluctantly said yes because I didn't want to cause an ordeal at the treatment center with my mom having to come and get me and everything. I honestly don't remember driving home that day. I don't know how I did it. My eyes were so clouded with tears the entire way home that I don't know how I saw where I was going. But I made it home, came through the front doors and immediately asked my mom if my therapist had called her yet. I was hoping that she had already talked to her so I wouldn't have to explain why I was such a mess.

I was crying so hard that it was hard to talk. It was even hard to breathe. But I eventually got the words out that I needed to say. My mom immediately called my dad, who immediately came home from work. They talked to me for a long time. My dad even called a suicide hotline and made me talk to the crisis responder, something I never in a million years thought I would have to do. While I was on the phone with them, my therapist called my mom. My therapist had also talked to my psychiatrist, and they recommended that my parents take me to the hospital the following morning. I had to stay with my mom at every moment until it was time for the assessment the next morning. I had to sleep in her bed, she had to come upstairs with me while I took a shower, she wouldn't leave my side. She was protecting me from myself.

Chapter Ten

GETTING BACK ON MY FEET

THE NEXT MORNING, MY MOM drove me to Marshall Pickens Hospital. Marshall Pickens Hospital isn't the typical hospital. It's not a hospital where people go for surgery or to get a cast put on a broken leg. Marshall Pickens is a psychiatric hospital.

My dad met us at the hospital, and we all walked into the lobby of the admissions center together. I didn't have much to say to them. I didn't have much to say to anyone. I felt numb to everything that was happening around me. I didn't want to talk. I didn't want to answer questions.

We waited out in the lobby until it was time to meet with a woman who worked in admissions. My parents and I went into her office where she began asking a long series of questions that I felt would never end. She asked me question after question and then asked my parents question after question. Then she asked me some questions alone without my parents in the room.

After all of the questions had been asked and answered, she went to meet with the child and adolescent psychiatrist to discuss what needed to take place. After waiting for what felt like forever, she finally came back and reported the news to us. I was being admitted, and my parents needed to go get the duffel bag that we had packed with clothes, just in case, out of the car.

It was scary. I didn't know or understand what was about to take place. I was still numb at that point, but my parents were noticeably upset. There wasn't a set time allotted for how long I was going to have to stay there. It was just going to depend on how things went. Then, everything finally hit me. I saw my dad crying, something that I rarely see. My mom was hysterical. The numbness finally went away. And instead of not feeling anything or just bottling everything up like I had been doing, I started to cry.

My family and I were led down a long hallway to the child and adolescent psychiatric unit. We walked in and waited again. It was then time to say good-bye to my parents. In that instant, despite all of the anger that I was feeling toward them for everything they had tried to make me eat over the previous months, I started to feel homesick. They hadn't even left yet. I was crying pretty hard, but I had no choice but to stay there.

My bag with my clothes had been taken from me. It had to be searched before I was allowed to have it back. Several clothing items that I had brought had to either go back home with my parents or had to be modified in order for me to have them there. For example, I had a pair of pajama pants that had a drawstring in them. Drawstrings or anything of that nature aren't allowed at Marshall Pickens because they could compromise the safety of the patients.

After everything was searched, I was able to go into what would be my bedroom for the next few days. It was nothing fancy at all. There was a twin bed with a ratty green blanket on it. There was a round table with two chairs. There was a small closet without a door, and then I was lucky enough to be in one of the only two rooms that had its own bathroom. I sat down on the bed and immediately longed for my bed back at home. This mattress was not very comfortable at all. I took the green blanket off and replaced it with my own blanket from home. I was delivered a tray of food from the cafeteria. Since I had just arrived, I didn't have the privilege yet of being able to leave the unit to go get my own food from the cafeteria.

I picked at my lunch, not necessarily due to my ED but simply because the hospital food was not very tasty. After eating, I don't remember much of what I did, but I know that at one point I met with the psychiatrist and got to talk to her about what was going on. Then I journaled a little bit, and eventually it was time for me and the other patients who were there to have group therapy.

Our days mainly consisted of being given assignments to do that helped us reflect on why we were there, getting food from the cafeteria, meeting with the psychiatrist, and having free time. Free time wasn't necessarily free time though. When you are in a psychiatric hospital, there isn't freedom to do much of anything. Many things were off-limits. But there were plenty of puzzles and board games that we were allowed to play.

It was a strange feeling, sitting around a table doing puzzles with other teenagers who were in similar yet different situations to mine. While we had a lot of differences in backgrounds, we all had one thing in common . . . we were at Marshall Pickens Hospital because we had thought about ending our lives and we were working through that.

I realized during this time that puzzles are actually very therapeutic and a good stress reliever. You don't think about much else when you're working on a puzzle. You just think about what piece you need to go where, what fits with what other piece, and what doesn't. There is a lot of trial and error. And eventually you finish, and the whole picture comes together.

Time seemed to stand still inside the walls of Marshall Pickens. I checked the time often. I would think that hours had gone by, when in reality, only about thirty minutes had passed. My favorite part of the day was each night at 6:00. At that time, we were allowed to have our parents come and visit us. During the hour of family visitation, I think my parents and I both started to understand each other more. They realized that my eating disorder wasn't something that we could just wish away. It was going to take time, effort, and encouragement for me to get better. They understood that I still had a lot to work on, and I understood that they wanted me to get better more than anything else. They wanted the old Marion back.

It was hard watching them leave each night when visitation time was over. But it gave me motivation to get back home so that I could spend time with them without being in a hospital.

I was admitted to Marshall Pickens on a Tuesday, and thankfully by that Friday, there was the possibility that I would be discharged that evening. I didn't want to have to spend the weekend there. I wanted more than anything to go home. Being there helped me, but

I just wanted to be back in my own home with my own shower, my own bed, my dogs, and my family. I wouldn't have stayed in the hospital if I had another choice.

At 7:00 pm on Friday, October 24, my parents walked back through the doors of the unit, and unlike the nights before, I was going to be able to leave with them. I couldn't wait. I gave them huge hugs when they walked in, and I could tell they were just as excited as I was that I was coming home. All of my discharge papers were signed, and it was time for me to leave.

My mom told me that bringing me home from the hospital this time was just as exciting as when she had brought me home from the hospital the first time . . . the day I was born.

It was time for a new beginning. A new start. A second chance at life. A chance at life that I wouldn't have gotten if I had followed through with any of the plans that I had written in my journal.

In the car, my parents told me that we were going to one of my favorite restaurants. The restaurant we were going to was a favorite both while I was struggling with my ED and when I wasn't. It all just depended on what I would order. However, I had already eaten dinner at the hospital, so I didn't want to go out to eat.

Now, the food at the hospital was nowhere near as good as the food would be at the restaurant, but still, I had already eaten dinner. But my parents insisted that we go.

We arrived and sat down at a table. As soon as we sat down, I looked at the door and noticed some familiar faces walking into the restaurant. I saw the faces of two kids I babysat and their parents. I have babysat these kids since I was in 6th grade, and I consider them my little sister and brother. They are close family friends of ours.

I didn't really think anything of it. I just thought they had the same idea my parents had—to eat out that night. But then it hit me . . . they were there to see me! I ran to the door and picked Maddie up and squeezed her tight, and she squeezed back even harder. Even Bennett, who is sometimes "too cool" for hugs as an elementary-school-aged boy, gave me a big hug. Then their parents, Jana and Kyle, did as well. I beamed as we all sat down at a big table. In that moment, I started to realize that I was loved a lot more than I knew, not only from how excited my parents were for me to be with them but also from how excited the kids were to see me. I would be missed if I were gone. People did care. People wanted to help me. I just had to be open to letting them help me, and I had to want help myself.

That was one thing I learned while I was in the hospital, that if things were going to get better, I had to want them to get better with every fiber of my being. No one could decide for me that things needed to get better. No one could eat for me. No one could deal with my depression for me. I had to take it into my own hands and truly decide that living a life controlled by my ED and depression wasn't truly a life that I wanted to live. Like a note that my mom left for me in the hospital said, "You have to choose to take the chance if you want anything to change." I had to decide to take a chance and try recovery if things were ever going to get better. And coming out of the hospital, I was certain that I was ready to take that chance. What did I have to lose?

When it was time to order, I was planning not to order anything and just sit there and enjoy the conversation. But at the last minute, I decided to order a piece of chocolate peanut butter cheesecake.

Everyone's food and my cheesecake came out, and I enjoyed every bite of my cheesecake. It was really ironic that cheesecake was my first meal coming out of the hospital, considering that before going in, I wouldn't have touched that cheesecake in a million years. But it also showed that I was ready for things to change.

Chapter Eleven

THE NEW ME

COMING OUT OF THE HOSPITAL didn't miraculously cure me. There wasn't any magic in the walls, in the water, or even in the food there. But I will say that had I not gone there, my story could have taken a very different turn. I firmly believe that God always has a plan for everything in our lives, no matter how bad. God used the time that I spent at Marshall Pickens to show me that I still had a lot of life in store for me. He showed me that He wasn't finished with me yet. And most importantly, He showed me that, yes, I had to make the decision for myself to recover and for things to improve, but He would be there with me every step of the way.

In a psychiatric hospital, the goal is stability. There aren't fun activities to do. Not much happens on a daily basis, except for talking every once in a while to psychiatrists and the occasional therapist. There is a lot of free time. During this free time, I had time to think and journal and reflect on the situation. My dad had brought my Bible on my first night there, and flipping through the pages provided comfort in the midst of despair and distress. I can't exactly say when a switch was flipped that made me decide to fight, but over the few days that I was there, I felt a very important shift in my thinking.

I didn't go from being suicidal and severely entrenched in an ED to being healed overnight. I didn't wake up the Saturday morning after being discharged to discover that I was completely fine. EDs and depression are a lot more complex issues that may take longer to work through. But the difference between the pre-hospital Marion and the post-hospital Marion was that the new Marion was ready to fight. The new Marion was ready to stand firm in who she was without her ED. The new Marion was ready to move on to bigger and better things. The new Marion didn't want to be held down by her mental illnesses.

So I chose to fight. When I would get anxious about what my family was having for dinner, I would remind myself that all food is simply fuel for my body. When I would look in the mirror and be tempted to critique every little part of my body, I would remind myself that I was an eighteen-year-old woman, and my body was supposed to look different from the way it had in years past. I would remind myself of the truth that I am fearfully and wonderfully made by a Creator who doesn't make mistakes.

I no longer felt that my existence on earth was a bad thing. I no longer felt that I would be stuck in a state of misery my entire life. I no longer felt that I didn't have a purpose. I felt confident. I felt joy. I felt a purpose.

In the weeks following my discharge from the hospital, I truly began to see that life had a lot more to offer me than I ever realized. Five days after I was discharged, my brother got engaged. I was finally going to have a sister. After growing up with two brothers, a sister was something I had always wanted. My family was entering a new season of life. Wedding plans were going to be made, and eventually the actual wedding would come. That was definitely something that I'm glad that I stuck around for.

My family also ended up going on a long-awaited vacation to Disney World in the months following my stay at Marshall Pickens. No longer was I afraid to go on vacation because of the many unknowns about eating out at restaurants and having unplanned treats here and there. I was excited to go to one of my favorite places in the world, and even more excited for Mickey Mouse ice cream bars after long days waiting in line to ride the Rock 'n' Rollercoaster again and again and again. Vacations while I was entrenched in my disorder were rough. It put a damper on the fun. It made everyone else miserable too. But this vacation was different, and I enjoyed every minute.

I also was able to resume my college search. There were several instances throughout my struggle when my parents and treatment team told me that there was a chance they wouldn't let me go off to college following my high school graduation. They weren't saying that to be mean or to make me mad, but it was simply out of love and protection. If I was not in a good place mentally, going to college would probably only make things worse. But after my parents finally saw that I was willing to do what I needed to do in order to get better, I was able to start thinking about college again. College visits were scheduled. We traveled to a few different places, and I ultimately decided on a small, private, Christian school: Anderson University.

I figured a small school would be a good place for me. It wouldn't be too overwhelming. I would be close to home if I needed to come back for anything. It was a Christian school that felt like a family from the first day that I toured. And on top of that, I was given the opportunity to become a collegiate athlete. I was given a spot on the cross country and track team.

The fact that I was even thinking about being able to run competitively truly showed that I was in a much different place. I made the decision to run track during my senior year of high school, and from that, I realized that I did love to run if I did it in a healthy way and not for the purpose of burning calories. Running was something that I thought I would never be able to do again. It was something that had caused me to slip so much that I was worried that I had lost it completely. But through a different mindset and through my dedication to living a full life outside of my ED, running became fun again. It became something that I enjoyed. It became a way to relieve stress. I started to love it again. So when I talked to the coach at Anderson and he offered me a spot on the team, I was flabbergasted. I was overjoyed. I never imagined that I would have that chance. But I got that chance. I was able to make a comeback.

No, I didn't get my times back down to where they were early on in high school. No, I wasn't a top runner on the team. No, I didn't win any races. But that isn't what mattered to me anymore. What mattered to me was that I was doing something that I loved and learning that my body and mind are a lot stronger than I knew. I remember lining up at the starting line of my first collegiate race and being amazed that I was there. I had gone from a girl who used running to become emaciated, to a girl who decided her junior year of high school that she hated running because she missed out on one state meet, to a girl who almost ended her life because she didn't feel like it was worth living, all the way to a girl who had shown herself and others that she had the strength within herself to blaze a new trail.

Anderson was great for me for my freshman year of college. It was a great way for me to get used to college life without being thrown into a huge school with thousands and thousands of people. I met a lot of great people, and I found the spark that I had deep within my heart for running that I thought had burned out long ago. However, after a little over a semester at Anderson, I was ready for something bigger. I was ready for the next step in my life. I decided that I wanted a school that was larger and had more going on.

With that being said, I made the hard decision to transfer schools for my sophomore year of college. I grew up being a Clemson fan, as both of my parents and one of my older brothers all graduated from Clemson. I grew up going to football games. I grew up dressing up as a tiger or a Clemson cheerleader for Halloween. I grew up dancing to the Clemson fight song . . . you get the point. I grew up a Tiger. So it was only natural that I decided that I was going to transfer to the greatest school (in my opinion) in the world, Clemson University.

That leads me to where I am today. I am currently studying psychology at Clemson University with the aspiration of one day becoming a therapist specializing in eating disorders. Although I did leave Anderson, I don't regret my time there at all. I believe that in our lives, we go through different stages where different choices might be beneficial at different times. And for me, being in a fragile state after going through so much in high school, it was important that I didn't throw myself into anything too quickly that could cause stress and anxiety and ultimately lead me to struggle again. I like to think of my year at Anderson as a year where I grew and learned a lot about myself and what I wanted out of life.

I realized that I wanted to be social. I realized that I wanted to go to Cook Out or Chick-fil-A late at night with friends and not be afraid to order a milkshake. I realized that I wanted to be in a football stadium with thousands of other people cheering just as hard for the Tigers as I was. I realized that I needed to push myself out of the small comfort zone that Anderson had become for me. I wanted to be involved. I wanted to make friendships that would last for a lifetime. I wanted to thrive. So for me, that meant submitting an application to Clemson University, one of the best decisions that I think I have made for myself in my entire life.

Chapter Twelve

HOW BEAUTY COMES FROM BROKENNESS

IF YOU'RE HUMAN, YOU'VE GONE through something difficult. I have yet to meet one person who has not dealt with some sort of hardship in life. You may not have struggled with an ED or depression, or maybe you have. But regardless of what you've been through, you've gone through something hard. I know I'm not alone in that. We live in a broken world full of life throwing trouble at us from all directions. Struggling isn't fun. Whether you have an ED, depression, anxiety, or any other mental illness, or if you have another struggle such as a problem within your family or career, I can guarantee that you don't think going through that is enjoyable. It isn't something that you would want someone else to have to deal with as well.

While I don't think that God enjoys seeing His children suffer and struggle, I think He uses our hardships to do many different things. I think He uses these struggles to teach us lessons, to help us rely on Him, and to show us a glimpse into our calling in life.

In my situation, I believe that God used my difficulties to do all of these things.

He taught me that I didn't have to be in control. Part of my eating disorder was rooted in me trying to have complete control over everything in my life. But, when we as humans try to have that control, things end up even more out of control than ever. This was my experience throughout my struggle. I tried so hard to have that sense of control, but my life ended up in shambles.

God taught me that no matter what I thought of the way I looked, that I was beautiful. Humans were created by God, in the image of God, to have a relationship with God. He is an artist who paints each of us uniquely the way He wants us. Could you imagine going up to an artist who was painting something and telling them that you didn't like what they painted? That would be rude and also hurtful to the artist. I like to believe that critiquing my body is the same as that.

God showed me that even in my hardest times, I need to rely on Him and not myself. Throughout my struggles, I always tried to rely on myself to get better. But that is exhausting and left me feeling even worse than I did to begin with. Relying on God can be hard sometimes in a culture that leans so heavily on being strong and independent and able to do things yourself, but there are some things that we literally can't do on our own. Letting people in on your struggles is important. Being vulnerable and open is hard, but there is freedom that comes from saying what has been welling up inside of you for so long. Being open with my parents and friends was a key factor in keeping me on the right path. I needed to rely on my family and friends, but more importantly, I needed to rely on God to bring me through my rough patch because I didn't have the strength, the will, or the capacity to get through it on my own.

Going through the struggle of dealing with an eating disorder and depression also revealed things to me that I may not have known otherwise. Like I said above, I believe that God can use our struggles to show us what our calling may be and to show us a reason for why we had to endure a painful time. In my case, I believe that it helped me to see what I wanted my future occupation to be. I decided that I wanted to become a therapist who specializes in eating disorders. I would have never known this had I not gone through what I did. If you've gone through something difficult, which is everyone reading this, you know how much better you feel after talking to someone who has experienced the same thing and has come out on the other side of it. They can understand and can relate. They can empathize. And it makes you feel less alone. I feel like my experiences will allow me to relate to my future clients in ways that I never would have been able to relate to them before.

Eating disorders are a lot more common than people may realize. I have come in contact with a countless number of people who either are struggling with an eating disorder or have struggled with an eating disorder and have been able to speak truth and encouragement into their lives. One day in one of my classes during my senior year of high school, we weren't doing anything, and everyone was on their phones. I had nothing else to do, and I got the idea to make a "recovery Instagram account." Instagram and all other forms of social media are littered with "thinspiration" pictures and accounts, "fitspiration" pictures and accounts, and "pro-ana" (pro-anorexia) or "pro-mia" (pro-bulimia) accounts. Not to mention, everywhere we look, someone is posting a picture with the hashtag "transformation Tuesday" to brag on how much weight they've lost or how "fit" they've gotten. Diet ads are everywhere. It's rare to see pictures, commercials, and social media accounts that promote balanced eating, loving your body for what it is, and a healthy relationship with exercise. I started my recovery Instagram account with no clue what would end up happening with it. My account grew to an account with close to 10,000 followers. Through telling my story, posting pictures and quotes on Instagram, and simply talking to other people and living my new life, I'm able to show that there is hope and healing and freedom, and that stories like mine can have a happy ending. Or in other words, a happy beginning of a new chapter in life.

Sometimes I think back to solving the puzzles in the hospital. The steps that go into solving a puzzle remind me a lot of what the whole recovery process is like. Sometimes, it's hard to find the right piece. Sometimes, you think the piece you have is the right one so you keep trying as hard as you can to make it fit, but it just doesn't. Sometimes a piece falls under the couch, and you have to wait until you find it again. But eventually, all of the pieces fall into place, and a beautiful picture starts to unfold.

I'm extremely thankful that the pieces to my life's puzzle have started to fall into place. A beautiful picture has started to be revealed. A picture that couldn't have unfolded without all the things that I've been through. A picture that has a middle school girl deciding that she wants to be in control of every morsel of food put in her mouth. A puzzle piece that has a state championship cross country trophy on it. A picture that has to do with being in a partial hospitalization program at The Riley Center. Or a piece that has to do with Marshall Pickens. A piece that says Anderson University. A tiger paw. A puzzle piece that shows my desire to help others. My puzzle contains a lot of different pieces so far. Some of the pieces aren't pleasant. Some are. But all put together, it creates something beautiful.

My puzzle isn't finished yet. As I grow and change, my story will continue to grow. My picture will gain new details here and there. I don't know what the final product will look like. But here's the thing . . . I have a God who knows each and every detail about what my picture will look like, and daily He helps me lay the pieces out.

Life truly is a beautiful thing. There is so much that we take for granted. But I promise you, the little things in life become the big things. So much has happened in my life that I wouldn't have experienced if things had gone differently for me. But here I am now, getting to live life in the way that God intended for me to live.

People often ask me if I wish that I had never had an eating disorder. I never planned for my eating disorder to happen. And if I could go back, and do anything to prevent it from happening, I would. However, with everything that happens in our lives, we can choose to be bitter about it happening, or we can grow from it and use it for a greater purpose. Am I glad that I struggled with an eating disorder? Of course not. But am I thankful for it? In a strange way, yes. I'll end with a quote that I've heard numerous times throughout these past few years: "I'm thankful for my struggle, because without it, I wouldn't have found my strength."

Chapter Thirteen

PHASES FROM MOM'S PERSPECTIVE

AFTER HAVING TWO BOYS AND finding out through our ultrasound that our third child would be a girl, I jokingly told my doctor that I hoped I knew how to raise a girl. He laughed and told me not to worry because she would teach me. He didn't know at the time how true that statement would be. She's turned out to be a great teacher!

From the time that Marion's personality developed, it was obvious she was going to be a spunky and fun little girl. She was always happy! Being the baby girl and having two older brothers, she was just a wee bit spoiled! She loved to sing, dance, play with Barbies, play dress up, and have play dates with friends. She was hauled around to all of her brothers' sporting events but was a great sport about it as long as we had a baby doll in tow and some snacks. She loved clothes, shoes, and hair bows, and she was a total ham in front of the camera. A little sassy pants princess toddler!

As she started school she made friends easily and was a great student. Her teachers always had nice things to say about her. We often heard the words *responsible, respectful,* and *caring,* which made us proud. She stayed busy taking dance and piano, playing soccer and basketball, and she loved her church activities. She also loved her friends, her big brothers, dogs, and going out to eat. Just loved life. Basically the perfect life for a growing girl. In middle school that all drastically changed, and we soon wished we had a magic wand to bring back the happy days.

Typical for Marion, as she entered middle school, she wanted to be involved. Even though busy, she always had great grades and was very independent and responsible with her schoolwork. She enjoyed reading, and we noticed she loved to write stories and illustrate her work. Most stories were fictional, but you could tell they were based on her experiences. Little did we know at the time that one day she would write a real book—based on her experiences.

We noticed a considerable weight loss around Thanksgiving of her eighth grade year. She wasn't overweight to begin with; however, we could see a change. She had started running cross country and was running daily, so we just attributed that to the exercise.

Life was busy at the time. Our boys had golf tournaments, basketball games, and football games. I was teaching school, Rob was working hard, we were about to move into another house, and the holidays were approaching. Rob and I talked about the change we were noticing in Marion but decided to get through the holidays and keep an eye on her. We noticed through December that she wasn't eating much, and things she usually begged me to cook, she didn't want. Restaurants she used to love to go to were out of the question. There was always an excuse. I remember telling her one day that I was worried and asked her if she was aware of eating disorders. Although I didn't know a thing about it, I had heard of it. She seemed miffed that I brought that up, but she assured me she was fine. At that point I didn't think there was a problem, and if there was, I was sure we could fix it! We continued to stay busy with everyday life.

The problem I didn't think was real wouldn't go away. The weight loss continued, and we noticed her moving food around on her plate at mealtime to make it look like she was eating. Rob and I decided it was time to take action and get her to the doctor. She was willing to go, thankfully. We questioned ourselves at the time as to why we didn't intervene sooner, but I think we really thought it was some weird phase that would soon pass. Actually, I think as parents we were in a phase ourselves . . . Denial!

Upon the realization that we did indeed have a problem that needed attention, we began our journey seeking help. When you know nothing about eating disorders other than that they happen to other people, who do you call for help? We started with our pediatrician, who then referred us to a local therapist. We saw therapists, nutritionists, and doctors . . . day by day . . . week by week . . . month by month . . . which turned into years.

These years were extremely stressful for me, Rob, Austin, and Crawford. What happened to that fun little girl who kept us constantly entertained? How did this happen? Was it something I caused by saying something about myself needing to exercise or run more because I felt I was gaining weight? Had we caused this in some way because we enjoyed running? Denial turned to guilt. I felt we were constantly asking Marion if she could pinpoint what triggered all of this, and she simply could not name anything.

Not only were we working on improving her eating habits and increasing her weight, but we were also trying to deal with the sad, lonely, moody person that lived in our house. We just had to get out of the guilt phase. It was getting us nowhere, and we had to focus on getting Marion well.

The next phase as I see it was the pain phase. Pure physical and emotional pain. Crying so hard that I made myself sick. That feeling that there was a big black cloud over our house. Marion totally withdrew from the life we knew as normal. She just wanted to sleep, dreaded going to school, didn't want to socialize, would not cooperate at meal times, and wore a permanent frown on her face. She lost all her friends. I was angry at the time because I felt others should notice she was hurting, and that was a time she needed her friends the most. However, from living with her and seeing the change in her, I realized her friends must not understand. I'm sure they thought she was acting odd, because she was. No one wants to hang around someone who seems so sad . . . especially in high school!

For the longest time she didn't want anyone to know what she was going through, and it wasn't something we were comfortable sharing for quite some time. One night after another tearful conversation, she blurted out that she just wished she had someone to talk to besides us or her therapists, but there was no one. Her friends were gone. I explained to her that maybe she should try to reach out to some of them and explain. She began to tell some friends, but things didn't get much better. In fact, maybe things got worse.

Marion allowed me to tell a few of my closest friends. I did. I needed someone to talk to besides Rob. Rob and I talked a lot, but we were living it day to day, and we both needed an outlet as this sort of caused us to withdraw socially as well.

Someone shared with me once that Marion's friends might be turning away because she was telling them about her struggles. I remember wanting to scream! Marion needed to talk about it! She wanted to explain why she had withdrawn. Why couldn't people understand that? Why was I so angry at them for not understanding? I had no answer because I couldn't understand any of this myself.

So, enter the anger phase. How could this happen to our sweet girl? Why did friends desert Marion when she was so sad and lonely? Why couldn't the therapists and doctors fix this quickly? Rob and I were constantly trying to figure out the next plan of action and often disagreed on what was best, therefore causing conflict between us.

That black cloud stayed over us. Although Marion maintained her high grades, she totally missed out on the social aspects of high school. She hardly spoke at home, slept a lot, and was aggravated when anyone tried to make her smile. She hated the sound of the dogs barking, and everything we did or said irritated her. We calmed her through crying spells, and then I would go cry in my room. She experienced panic attacks and had trouble breathing. Her hair was falling out. This was getting old.

Anger phase moved to frustration phase. We were providing every outlet of help that we could afford but just felt stuck. Thank goodness for insurance, as this could have destroyed us financially. We involved ourselves in family counseling, and it usually ended up with me crying so hard I couldn't speak as I depleted the therapist's facial tissue supply. Marion just seemed to stare at me with a blank stare when I was upset. She would apologize for putting us in this situation, but there didn't seem to be anything she could do about it.

Marion's psychiatrist actually propelled us into the next phase. It could be named the take-care-of-business phase. Although it was probably the worst phase emotionally, it didn't linger as long as the other phases we had previously experienced. When Marion's depression sent her to rock bottom, her psychiatrist recommended we take her to be evaluated for admittance in a facility that could help her with her depression. She had carried this burden too long, and her depression became overwhelming. So, again, who do you call when you have never had to do this before? We had only two local options, and the first place we called did not have any availability at the time. The other option was the adolescent mental facility at the hospital.

Hearing that it was necessary for her to be admitted was devastating, but we knew it was necessary. I don't know if I've ever cried that hard in my life. I remember thinking that while other parents I knew were filling out paperwork for their child's senior year, we were filling out paperwork for our child to be admitted to a hospital! When we were asked to leave, Marion's blank stare turned to a frightened look accompanied by lots of tears. All Rob and I could do was hug her with all of our might because we were crying so hard we couldn't speak. We were allowed to visit her once every evening for a limited time, but saying good-bye was horrible because we had no idea how long she would have to stay there.

Marion had several sessions with a psychiatrist while there. On the fourth day we received a call from the doctor, saying that she felt Marion was okay to come home and that she was expressing a desire to be well and to say no to her eating disorder. We would still need to continue medication for depression and see therapists, but she noted a positive change in Marion's disposition. I will never forget that afternoon returning to get my girl. She greeted us with the happiest face and a tight sincere hug. She and I actually skipped back to the car together, and I told her I felt the same joy I had experienced bringing her home from the hospital as a newborn.

A feeling of hope and happiness was taking hold. That take-care-of-business phase was short, thankfully! We had prayed and prayed for this. The dessert she ordered that night when we went to dinner with friends was another sign that she was going to be okay! I've never seen a piece of cheesecake that big, and she ate the whole thing!

Enter the hope phase. This too was one of the shorter phases as I saw Marion take a grip on her recovery.

I am proud to say that at this point in her sophomore year in college, my sassy pants princess is back and in full force! After a long battle, we are in the victory phase. Although she experienced a roller coaster of events, changes, and emotions, there was one thing that remained constant . . . her FAITH. She strapped on her armor and fought through it . . . but not alone . . . with God! He had a plan for her! His plan led her to what she is doing today, which is sharing her story, hoping to help others. Whether it is through her Instagram account, her book, talking with friends who are struggling with this illness, or majoring in psychology with plans to be an eating disorder therapist, Marion is determined to help others. She knows how blessed she is to have come through this and truly enjoy life. She wants so badly for others to know they can too! This is her passion! She says she never wants to go back to the dark times.

We've learned that having an eating disorder is not about telling someone to go eat a cheeseburger and it will all be okay. It's a very serious disease with numerous physical and emotional side effects. It doesn't just affect the patient. It affects family, friends, and relationships. We've learned so much about this horrible illness that seems to be running rampant with females and males of all ages. We've learned statistics that are startling, and we know that this illness has taken the lives of many. Most of all, we learned a lot from our daughter, just as my doctor said we would when she was born. We knew she was a great girl, but we've seen even more greatness come from her with her desire to share her story in hopes that she could be a light for others and her not being afraid to share her faith as part of her journey. We love seeing her enjoy college to the fullest, establishing new friendships, getting reacquainted with old friends, taking selfies with her sorority sisters, and cheering at football games. She loves her dogs, shopping, and her big brothers, *and* her new sister-in-law. She always wanted a sister!

Life is good. She's back!

We appreciate all of the doctors, therapists, nutritionists, family, and friends who were there for us during that time. Thank you for listening and offering prayers. I can't express enough how much I appreciate Austin and Crawford for being there for their little sister when she needed them. Special thanks to her former youth group leader Darren DePaul for providing spiritual support and his listening ear for Marion before, during, and after; to her doctor and our friend, Dr. Scott Dobson, for medical care, encouraging words, and being available at ALL hours; and to our dear friend Jana Candler for her constant friendship to our family and love for Marion—and especially for crying with me! Each person involved was part of God's plan! He's been there beside us in the bad phases and led us to the best phase ever. We have VICTORY! Praise God from whom all blessings flow!

For more information about

Marion Reeves

and

Perfectly Imperfect
please visit:

marionreeves12@yahoo.com
Instagram: marionreeves12
www.facebook.com/perfectlyimperfectbymarionreeves
www.facebook.com/marion.reeves2

For more information about
AMBASSADOR INTERNATIONAL
please visit:

www.ambassador-international.com
@AmbassadorIntl
www.facebook.com/AmbassadorIntl